Are You SMARTER Than Your KID?

Are You SMARTER Than Your KID?

The *Child Genius* Family Quiz Book

First published in Great Britain in 2018 by

Quercus Editions Ltd
Carmelite House
50 Victoria Embankment
London EC4Y 0DZ

An Hachette UK company

A CIP catalogue record for this book is available
from the British Library

HB ISBN 978 1 78747 661 5
Ebook ISBN 978 1 78747 660 8

10 9 8 7 6 5 4 3 2 1

Design & Typeset by www.andreanelli.com

Printed and bound in Great Britain by Clays Ltd, Elcograf S.p.A.

Contents

QUIZ 2

QUIZ 8   222

How
to use this book

Are You Smarter Than Your Kid? is inspired by Channel 4's *Child Genius*, and is divided into ten quizzes. Each of these has eight sections that roughly mirror the journey of the child geniuses as they progress through the annual competition:

- ❏ Spelling
- ❏ Comprehension
- ❏ Mental Maths
- ❏ Mensa Challenge
- ❏ History
- ❏ General Knowledge
- ❏ Science
- ❏ Advanced Language
- ❏ Sudden Death

Like the competitors on the television programme, you'll
probably have your own favourite rounds and ones that
you dread facing. There is no escape though – you have to
attempt each section to reach the end of the quiz! Questions
in the General Knowledge, History and Science rounds get
progressively harder, so that by the end of the round, you
really will know whether you're a true child genius or not.
The book is intended for the whole family to tackle, but there
are different ways of using it. You could attempt the questions
by yourself or in a group and decide just how smart (child
or otherwise) you are. Or, as we suggest, you can nominate
someone to be your very own Richard Osman (although
clearly not every questioner has to be a 6ft 7in Cambridge
graduate), whilst everyone else answers questions either on
their own or in teams, depending on how many players there
are. Scores (one per correct answer) are totted up at the end
of the quiz and the family/group brainiac is crowned.

The only equipment you'll need is a timer of some sort – either
a phone or an egg timer from a board game. If the buzzer

makes a sound at the end of the round, all the more fun! We
suggest that you agree a time limit for each round or question,
according to the round. In the programme, most take four
to five minutes, varying with the number of questions being
asked. For single spelling questions you should allow about a
minute. It is entirely up to you what rules you set but here are
a couple of fun and important rules from the programme:

- ❏ Only three passes per round, after which you have to attempt
  an answer…say anything; make something up!
- ❏ When the buzzer sounds at the end of the round you have
  up to 30 seconds to finish answering the question you were
  on…make the most of that thinking time, but make sure you
  don't take too long!

A pen and paper for the players or teams is essential. There
is a 'notes' section at the back of the book, and an optional
extra is a camera phone. Some questions (in the Mensa
Challenge section, for example) ask players to identify the
number of squares or triangles in a shape. This is where a

camera phone could come in handy – instead of every player taking it in turns to look at the same page, each can take a photograph and count away from the comfort of their own chair.

Answers are at the end of each quiz, so that each is discreet. That means if the questioner changes, the previous quizmaster won't know the answers to the new section.

And that's all there is to it! As Richard would say, 'Best of luck to you all'.

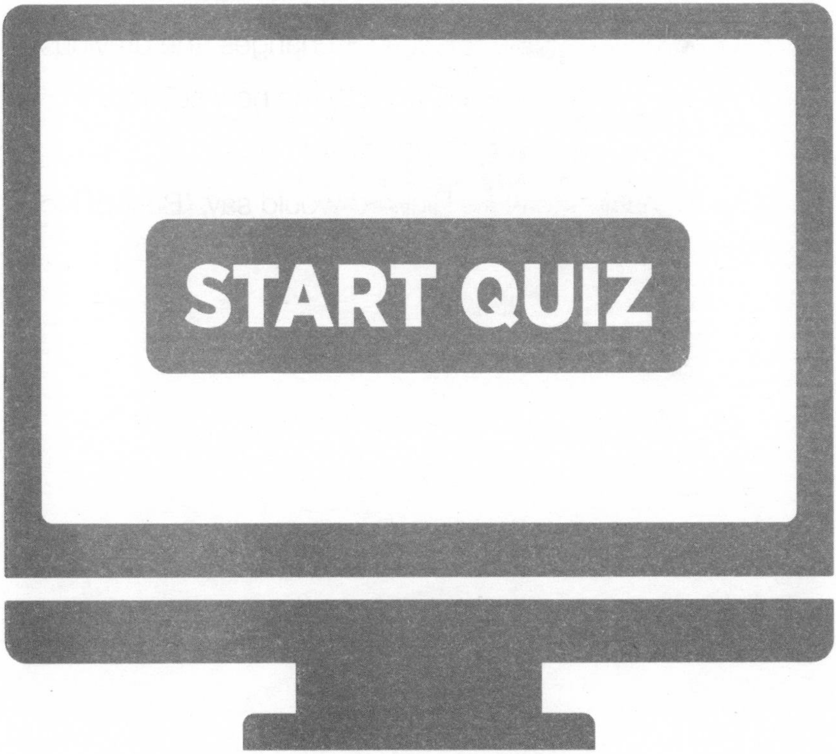
START QUIZ

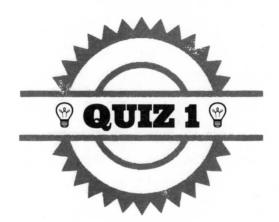

SPELLING

Spell the following five words:

1. **PHILIPPIC (PRON: FIL-LIP-PICK):**

    a bitter attack or denunciation, especially a verbal one.

    EXAMPLE: The candidate ended his campaign with a bitter philippic against his opponent.

2. **DISSIPATE (PRON: DISS-EH-PATE):**

    1. (to a feeling or emotion) disappear or cause to disappear. 2. waste or fritter away. 3. cause (energy) to be lost through its conversion to heat.

    EXAMPLE: After the leak the gas was allowed to dissipate.

3. **METALLURGY (PRON: MEH-TAL-UH-JEE):**

    the branch of science and technology concerned
    with the properties of metals and their production and
    purification.

    EXAMPLE: Experts in metallurgy were called in the
    court case regarding the factory pipe failure.

4. **LASSITUDE (PRON: LASS-I-TUDE):**

    a state of physical or mental weariness; lack of energy.

    EXAMPLE: Jenny was so overcome with lassitude, she
    retired to bed.

5. **INQUILINE (PRON: IN-QUILL-LINE):**

    an animal exploiting the living space of another.

    EXAMPLE: Having overstayed his welcome at his
    friend's house, Jacob felt like an inquiline.

COMPREHENSION

Pick the correct definition of the following words:

1. **LAGOMORPH (PRON: LAG-UH-MORF)**

   a) A lagomorph, probably a rabbit, ate all the cabbages in the garden.

   b) Moira lay on the lagomorph for three hours, hoping to top up her tan.

   c) To lagomorph a tree, you must equip yourself with a huge saw.

2. **SAMOVAR (PRON: SAM-UH-VAH)**

   a) The church congregation bowed their heads as the samovar was read.

   b) Whilst on holiday in Moscow, Jim bought a samovar to take home to his mum.

   c) The car engine spluttered and Graeme knew that the samovar had broken.

3.   FRUGIVORE (PRON: FREW-JI-VOR)

a) Frugivore is a collarless sleeveless dress worn over clothes to keep them clean.

b) Steering a frugivore on the high seas is extremely difficult and tiring.

c) The frugivore flew into the garden to feast on the laden fruit trees.

4.   DILLETANTE (PRON: DILL-I-TAN-TE)

a) The dilettante is a small beetle which survives on cow manure.

b) Hugo is a bit of a dilettante as far as wine is concerned.

c) Aunt Irene visited her local dilettante every week to buy cooked meats, cheeses and olives.

5.   CHERVIL (PRON: CHUR-VILL)

a) The blacksmith uses a chervil to make horse shoes.

b) The umpire checked the height of the net with his chervil.

c) The award-winning chef added the herbs chervil and parsley to the dish before serving the food to his guests.

MENTAL MATHS

MULTIPLICATION

1. 85 x 9 =

2. 87 x 7 =

3. 83 x 8 =

ADDITION

1. 58 + 15 + 26 + 90 =

2. 93 + 51 + 77 + 67 =

3. 82 + 43 + 85 + 16 =

SUBTRACTION

1. 990 - 93.9 =

2. 549 - 70.2 =

3. 629 - 87.3 =

DIVISION

1. $58.8 \div 6 =$
2. $44.4 \div 4 =$
3. $65.1 \div 7 =$

MIXED CALCULATIONS

1. $12 \times 6 - 16 \times 4 =$
2. $12 \times 5 - 14 \times 5 =$
3. $11 \times 5 - 18 \times 6 =$

MENSA CHALLENGE

1. Famine is to food as drought is to:

   a) weather

   b) drinking

   c) water

2. How many more 9s are in the box than 1s?

7	4	8	6	5	0	1	66
22	9	6	0	8	5	8	9
6	4	55	2	1	2	0	7
8	1	5	4	5	3	2	9
0	33	6	9	5	8	4	0

3. What is the missing number? 54, 63, 72, ?, 90, 99

4. Liquid soap must be diluted 1 part soap to 8 parts water. In millilitres, how much liquid soap is there in 180ml of mix?

5.   How many triangles can you see?

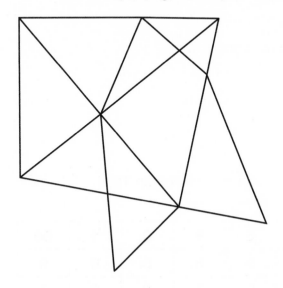

6.   Add one letter to complete one word and start the other:
      BEL (...) APE

7.   If A = 1, B = 2, C = 3 and so on, what is the total value
      of the word BOW?

8.   What is the next number? 89, 55, 34, 21, 13, ?

9. A recipe uses 300g sugar, 400g butter and 700g flour to make 70 biscuits. In grams, how much flour is used in each biscuit?

10. How many squares can you see?

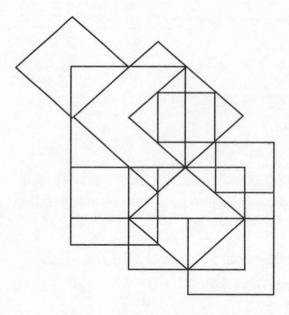

HISTORY

1. On 21 September 1792, France abolished its monarchy and established what in its place?

2. In which city was the Bastille, a fortress, stormed by the people in July 1789?

3. Which ancient hero appeared on the coinage of the French Revolution?

4. Which general became a dictator in Spain as a result of the Spanish Civil War?

5. Which Greek philosopher's work included *The Apology*, *The Republic* and *The Laws*?

6. Senegal gained independence from which country in August 1960?

7. The Holy League established by Pope Julius II was set up against which country?

8. After his banishment from Athens, the statesman Themistocles was made governor of which city by the Persians?

9. Which independent candidate received 18.5 per cent of the vote in the 1992 American election?

10. Which early Greek philosopher was the first person to explain a solar eclipse?

GENERAL KNOWLEDGE

1. From central Africa, which large bird lays the world's biggest eggs?

2. What is the name of a giant ocean wave caused by a sudden movement of the ocean floor which can often trigger an earthquake?

3. What is the name of the Caribbean country whose capital city is Kingston?

4. What is the name of the hottest planet in our solar system?

5. From which UK city did *Titanic* leave on its maiden voyage to New York?

6. Water is a compound of two chemical elements. Hydrogen is one, what is the other?

7. Which composer wrote the classical piece *The Four Seasons*?

8. Mount Cook is the highest mountain in which country?

9. What discovery was made in China in 1974 consisting of around 8,000 life-sized figures?

10. Its capital is Cairo, but what is the name of this north African country?

11. What is the name of the lowest region of the atmosphere, bounded by the Earth beneath and the stratosphere above?

12. Olympus Mons is the largest known volcano in our solar system, but on which planet would you find it?

13. Which mountain in the Alps is known as Monte Cervino in Italian and Mont Cervin in French?

14. The Very Large Array is the world's largest radio telescope consisting of 27 dishes, but in which US state is it situated?

15. In which year did table tennis become an Olympic sport?

SCIENCE

1.   Amphibians, birds and fish are all examples of what taxonomic rank?

2.   As used in IR radiation, what does IR stand for?

3.   Ninety-six per cent of the planet Saturn's atmosphere is made up of which element?

4.   A plant that grows again from the ground up each year is what sort of perennial?

5.   Compared to microwaves, are the wavelengths of visible light shorter, the same or longer?

6.   At 4.2 light years' distance, which star is closest to the Sun?

7. At Saturn's north pole, there is a cloud formation in which mathematical shape?

8. Carina, Dumbbell and Rosette are all examples of what sort of interstellar clouds?

9. Anadromous fish live in the sea, but breed in rivers. What sort of fish do the opposite?

10. At almost 4.4 light years' distance, which is the closest binary star system to the Sun?

ADVANCED LANGUAGE

Solve the following five anagrams:

1. **s c i c h y p**

   Sensitive to parapsychological forces or influences.

2. **i o n e r q u s t e i a n**

   A written or printed form used in gathering information on some subject or subjects.

3. **h o n e b a p i x o**

   A strong and unreasonable dislike or fear of people from other countries.

4. **c e d q u i n a t a**

   On terms of familiarity but not intimacy.

5. **s t o p s h a m r o m i e**

   A complete change of physical form or substance.

SUDDEN DEATH

35% of 300 =

ANSWERS

COMPREHENSION

1.   a) A lagomorph, probably a rabbit, ate all the cabbages in the garden.
      DEF: a mammal of the order *Lagomorpha*, which comprises hares, rabbits and pikas.

2.   b) Whilst on holiday in Moscow, Jim bought a samovar to take home to his mum.
      DEF: a highly decorated tea urn used in Russia.

3.   c) The frugivore flew into the garden to feast on the laden fruit trees.
      DEF: an animal that feeds on fruit.

4.   b) Hugo is a bit of a dilettante as far as wine is concerned.
      DEF: a person who cultivates an area of interest, such as the arts, without real commitment or knowledge.

5. c) The award-winning chef added the herbs chervil and
    parsley to the dish before serving the food to his guests.
    DEF: a Eurasian plant of the parsley family, with delicate fern-
    like leaves which are used as a culinary herb.

MENTAL MATHS

Multiplication

1. 765
2. 609
3. 664

Addition

1. 189
2. 288
3. 226

Subtraction

1. 896.1
2. 478.8
3. 541.7

Division

1. 9.8
2. 11.1
3. 9.3

Mixed Calculations

1. 224
2. 230
3. 222

MENSA CHALLENGE

1. Water
2. 1
3. 81
4. 20ml (1 part soap/8 parts water (9), each part = 20ml; 8 x 20ml = 160ml, therefore 1 part of water = 20ml).
5. 19
6. BEL (T) APE
7. 40
8. 8
9. 10g (700 ÷ 70 = 10)
10. 17

HISTORY

1. Republic (ACCEPT: First Republic)
2. Paris
3. Hercules (ACCEPT: Heracles)
4. (Francisco) Franco
5. Plato
6. France
7. France
8. Magnesia
9. Ross Perot
10. Anaxagoras

GENERAL KNOWLEDGE

1. Ostrich
2. Tsunami
3. Jamaica
4. Venus
5. Southampton
6. Oxygen
7. Vivaldi

8.   New Zealand
9.   The Terracotta Army
10. Egypt
11. Troposphere
12. Mars
13. Matterhorn
14. New Mexico
15. 1988

SCIENCE

1.   Classes
2.   Infrared (ACCEPT: infrared radiation)
3.   Hydrogen
4.   Herbaceous
5.   Shorter
6.   Proxima Centauri (ACCEPT: 'Alpha Centauri C'; if they say Alpha Centauri, prompt: 'I need you to be more specific, please')
7.   Hexagon
8.   Nebulas (ACCEPT: nebulae)

9. Catadromous
10. Alpha Centauri

ADVANCED LANGUAGE

1. psychic
2. questionnaire
3. xenophobia
4. acquainted
5. metamorphosis

SUDDEN DEATH

105

☀ Did You Know? ☀

Mensa's 17 Signs of a Child Genius

Are you a child, or the parent of a child, who asks questions all the time, is up to speed on current affairs, likes to change and update the rules of a game and is not satisfied with anything less than full marks? Then read on.

The High IQ Society, Mensa, believes there are 17 signs that could point to a child genius and have put together a checklist of what to look out for. This is part of their commitment to spotting and nurturing intelligence and supporting gifted children and their parents. Whilst it is unlikely that anyone would display all 17 features, there are several that stand out as clear indicators of exceptional ability – like an amazing memory, reading early, learning easily and showing expertise in specialist subjects. Less positive on the list are the intolerance of other children, impossible goal setting and the need to be in control. Take a look at the list below…

- ❏ An unusual memory
- ❏ Pass intellectual milestones early
- ❏ Read early
- ❏ Unusual hobbies or interests or an in-depth knowledge of certain subjects
- ❏ Intolerance of other children
- ❏ An awareness of world events
- ❏ Set themselves impossibly high standards
- ❏ May be a high achiever
- ❏ Prefers to spend time with adults or in solitary pursuits
- ❏ Loves to talk
- ❏ Asks questions all the time
- ❏ Learns easily
- ❏ Developed sense of humour
- ❏ Musical
- ❏ Likes to be in control
- ❏ Makes up additional rules for games
- ❏ Extrovert/introvert

How many of these apply to you or someone you know?

SPELLING

Spell the following five words:

1. **LAPILLI (PRON: LAH-PILL-EYE):**

   rock fragments ejected from a volcano.

   EXAMPLE: Kalani brought for show-and-tell a jar of lapilli collected by her mother following an eruption of the volcano.

2. **RUBESCENT (PRON: ROO-BESS-SANT):**

   reddening; blushing.

   EXAMPLE: Gloria's rubescent cheeks made obvious her embarrassment.

3. **CINEREOUS (PRON: SIN-NEAR- REE-US):**

   (especially of hair or features) ash-grey.

   EXAMPLE: The stems are covered with several barks or rinds, the latter being of a cinereous dirt colour and very thin.

4. **SEPULCHRAL (PRON: SEP-PUHL- KRUL):**

   gloomy; dismal.

   EXAMPLE: Dusk and a vase of gardenias gave the parlour sitting room a sepulchral air.

5. **BODHRÁN (PRON: BOW-RAHN):**

   a shallow one-sided Irish drum, typically played using a short stick with knobbed ends.

   EXAMPLE: The bodhrán is similar in construction to popular African and Middle Eastern frame drums.

COMPREHENSION

Pick the correct definition of the following words:

1. **FLUMMERY (PRON: FLUM-UH-REE)**

   a) The journalist accused the politician of flummery and asked again for an answer to his question.

   b) The flummery of the exotic bird was very bright and impressive.

   c) A flummery is a manservant or footman.

2. **TRAMONTANA (PRON: TRAM-MON-TARNA)**

   a) The tramontana are the pair of parallel lines on a tennis court.

   b) She shivered with fear as the tramontana crept onto her hand.

   c) Marco's mum told him to wear a scarf on the Italian piste as the tramontana was icy cold.

3. **LUMBAGO (PRON: LUM-BAY-GO)**

   a) The lumbago is a Latin ballroom dance in which dancers stamp their feet rhythmically.

b) Lumbago causes more absences from work than any other illness.

c) When visiting Ireland, tourists insist on stopping to see the lumbago standing stones.

4. REDOLENT (PRON: RED-O-LENT)

a) As soon as Arthur stepped out of the car, the village was redolent of childhood memories.

b) Once the redolent was removed from the roof, the house looked much cleaner.

c) Hens are fed a mixture of corn and redolent to keep them healthy.

5. BYTOWNITE (PRON: BY-TOWN-ITE)

a) Everyone cheered loudly as the bytownite eventually took flight.

b) The rocks containing bytownite were of great interest to the geology students.

c) There is much less traffic going through the town since the bytownite was built.

MENTAL MATHS

MULTIPLICATION

1. $664.3 \times 7 =$

2. $626.6 \times 7 =$

3. $742.3 \times 9 =$

ADDITION

1. $55 + 15 + 89 + 15 + 26 + 77 =$

2. $86 + 55 + 99 + 13 + 14 + 33 =$

3. $78 + 60 + 95 + 46 + 92 + 94 =$

SUBTRACTION

1. $614 - 89.2 =$

2. $882 - 81.9 =$

3. $582 - 59.3 =$

DIVISION

1. $43.8 \div 6 =$
2. $91.7 \div 7 =$
3. $38.8 \div 4 =$

MIXED CALCULATIONS

1. $18 \times 7 - 10 \times 2 \div 4 =$
2. $22 \times 5 - 14 \times 4 \div 2 =$
3. $13 \times 3 - 29 \times 3 \div 6 =$

MENSA CHALLENGE

1. Blue is to lake as green is to:

   a) beach

   b) grass

   c) khaki

2. If A = 1, B = 2, C = 3 and so on, what is the total value of the word ZIP?

3. What is the missing number? 98, 87, 78, ?, 66, 63

4. A runner completes a 28km run in three and a half hours. Assuming the runner runs at a constant speed, what distance does he cover in an hour?

5.   How many squares can you see?

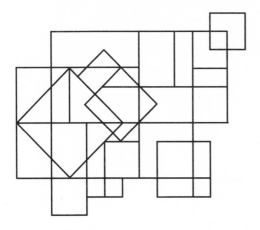

6.   Add one letter to complete one word and start the other:
      FOR (...) AID

7.   How many more 8s are there than 0s?

0	8	33	8	1	8	0	8
2	4	0	3	5	7	8	9
7	8	1	2	0	7	5	4
5	3	0	1	8	5	8	7
8	66	8	5	3	4	9	0

8.   What is the next number? 92, 80, 70, 62, 56, ?

9.   A mobile phone company offers 300 minutes for £5.
     How many minutes can be bought for £8?

10.   How many triangles can you see?

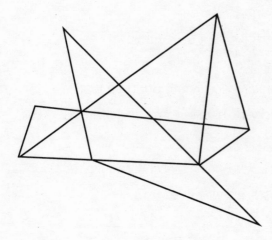

HISTORY

1. Hawaii became the 50th state of which country in 1959?

2. Which Danish author published his first book of fairy tales in 1835?

3. In which city was John F. Kennedy assassinated?

4. The Aristophanes play *Peace* is set during a war between Athens and which other state?

5. Where was Lyndon B. Johnson sworn in as the 36th US President?

6. In December 1998, Bill Clinton became only the second American president to be what?

7.   Which branch of government decides if the laws of the state have been followed or not?

8.   In 1494, Christopher Columbus set up a European colony at La Isabela. On which island?

9.   In which battle was the Macedonian king Antigonus killed in 301BC?

10.   Of which artistic 'brotherhood' were William Holman Hunt and John Everett Millais members?

GENERAL KNOWLEDGE

1. Occupying about a third of the surface of the globe, what is the largest ocean in the world?

2. What is the capital city of Belgium?

3. In which country were the first modern Olympic Games held?

4. Which mammals fly at night using echolocation to navigate?

5. What name is given to molten rock when it is underground?

6. What is the name of the scale used to measure the magnitude of an earthquake?

7. In which year was President John F. Kennedy assassinated?

8. In which country was the baroque composer, Antonio Vivaldi born?

9. In which country are children in remote areas taught through 'The School of Air', either by radio contact or online?

10. Broccoli, Brussels sprouts and cauliflower are all descended from which wild vegetable?

11. In which year was Alexander Graham Bell granted a patent for the first practical telephone?

12. What is the name of Japan's first space probe to Mars which failed in 1998?

13. What is the name of Thailand's capital city?

14. Where in the world would you find Mecca, the birthplace of Muhammad, the founder of Islam?

15. In which country is the largest winter carnival in the world celebrated?

SCIENCE

1. Evaporation involves a change of state from liquid to what?

2. How many atoms are there in total in a molecule of water?

3. In August 2013, what tune was played out loud on Mars by the Curiosity rover?

4. In which country is Baikonur, the largest rocket-launch site on Earth?

5. Of a substance's freezing, melting and boiling points, two are the same. Which is different?

6. Spirit and Opportunity are rovers that landed on which planet in 2004?

7. Tanning of the skin is caused by what type of radiation?

8. The Great Red Spot is a huge storm system on which planet?

9. Barnard's Star is in which constellation?

10. Dinitrogen tetroxide is a dimer formed from two molecules of what?

ADVANCED LANGUAGE

Solve the following five anagrams:

1. g r i d p o y

Someone young who has a great natural ability for something such as music, mathematics or sport.

2. f o r p e s s o n i

A job that requires advanced education or training.

3. b a r u l v e n l e

Weak and without protection.

4. s o r g a r e s g

The person, group, or country that starts a fight or battle.

5. v i o l i n c a b e n e c

Something that cannot be thought of, understood, imagined or believed.

SUDDEN DEATH

40% of 300 =

ANSWERS

COMPREHENSION

1.   a) The journalist accused the politician of flummery and
     asked again for an answer to his question.
     DEF: meaningless or insincere flattery or conventions.

2.   c) Marco's mum told him to wear a scarf on the Italian
     piste as the tramontana was icy cold.
     DEF: a cold north wind blowing in Italy or the adjoining
     regions of the Adriatic and Mediterranean.

3.   b) Lumbago causes more absences from work than any
     other illness.
     DEF: pain in the muscles and joints of the lower back.

4.   a) As soon as Arthur stepped out of the car, the village
     was redolent of childhood memories.
     DEF: strongly reminiscent or suggestive of.

5.　b) The rocks containing bytownite were of great interest to the geology students.

DEF: a mineral present in many basic igneous rocks, consisting of a calcic plagioclase feldspar.

MENTAL MATHS
Multiplication
1.　4650.1
2.　4386.2
3.　6680.7

Addition
1.　277
2.　300
3.　465

Subtraction
1.　524.8
2.　800.1
3.　522.7

Division

1. 7.3
2. 13.1
3. 9.7

Mixed Calculations

1. 58
2. 192
3. 5

MENSA CHALLENGE

1. Grass
2. 51 (26 + 9 + 16 = 51)
3. 71
4. 8km (28km ÷ 3.5 = 8km in an hour)
5. 21
6. FOR (M) AID

   NB: FORB/BAID; FORD/DAID; FORK/KAID; FORN/ NAID; FORR/RAID; FORS/SAID; FORT/TAID; FORW/ WAID. At least one in each pair is found in Oxford Online, but not in the *Oxford English Dictionary*, so would therefore not be allowed.

7. 4

8. 52

9. 480 (300 for £5, therefore £1 buys 60 minutes, 60 x 8 = 480/8 hours; but we ask for minutes, so no one should give the answer 8)

10. 18

HISTORY

1. United States of America (ACCEPT: USA/US)

2. Hans Christian Andersen

3. Dallas

4. Sparta

5. Air Force One (ACCEPT: on an aeroplane)

6. Impeached

7. The Judiciary

8. Hispaniola

9. Battle of Ipsus

10. Pre-Raphaelite Brotherhood

GENERAL KNOWLEDGE

1. Pacific Ocean

2. Brussels

3. Greece

4. Bats (DO NOT ACCEPT: flying fox)

5. Magma

6. Richter Scale

7. 1963

8. Italy

9. Australia

10. Cabbage

11. 1876

12. Nozomi

13. Bangkok

14. Saudi Arabia

15. Canada (Quebec City)

SCIENCE

1. Gas (ACCEPT: gaseous/gaseous vapour/vapour)

2. Three

3.   'Happy Birthday'

4.   Kazakhstan

5.   Boiling

6.   Mars

7.   Ultra-violet

8.   Jupiter

9.   Opiuchus

10. Nitrogen dioxide

ADVANCED LANGUAGE

1.   prodigy

2.   profession

3.   vulnerable

4.   aggressor

5.   inconceivable

SUDDEN DEATH

120

♀ Did You Know? ♀

How Memory Works

Our memories work in mysterious ways and continue to baffle scientists and the medical profession, despite all their research. There is still so much to discover about how memory is collected and then recalled. Why is it that we remember the oddest facts or moments and can forget crucial information? Understanding what we already know about the process can help us to strengthen our memories and trust them in the future.

The brain performs three functions to enable the successful recall of a memory. It has to register the experience, person or thing, which is known as **encoding**. Then it **consolidates** this information to store away until finally, it is called on to **retrieve** it. The success of this three-part process is reliant on the good behaviour of the **limbic system**, the

area of the brain that deals with recall and emotion. This is also where the strangely named **hippocampus** is located – a small organ with the big job of transforming short-term memory into long-term. If this organ is affected, it has a direct impact on memory, and its degeneration can cause diseases such as dementia and Alzheimer's.

This system of memory travels around a complicated mind map that we continually navigate. When we think of an object, a childhood holiday or a statistic, our brains are triggering a series of actions which pulls up information stored via a complex structure of cells. These nerve cells are called **neurons**. They are transmitted through special passages known as **synaptic connections** and message each other with the help of chemical-based **neurotransmitters**. The stronger the signal between the ten trillion-ish synapses, the more likely we are to imprint what we are experiencing as a memory. To enable us to then recall it means travelling at speed around our mind maps, visiting areas that could be responsible for fear, sound, place and smell, for example. The memory comes to us in one piece, as if from one place, but it has taken several areas of your brain to summon it up.

It is important to maintain memory by continuing to work it, pushing the process to function as highly as possible through challenges, education and adventures. Without this, our brain pathways start to slow down and we can lose them entirely as we age. Put simply, use it or lose it.

SPELLING

Spell the following five words:

1. **MULTIFARIOUS (PRON: MULTI-FARE-EE-US):**
   many and of various types.
   EXAMPLE: The multifarious activities at the interactive museum make it a place that everyone can enjoy.

2. **BARRACUDA (PRON: BARRA-KYOO-DA):**
   a large predatory tropical marine fish with a slender body and large jaws and teeth.
   EXAMPLE: Julia considered the barracuda to be the most fearsome fish at the aquarium.

3. **CONTUSION (PRON: CON-CHOO-SHUN):**
   a region of injured tissue or skin in which blood capillaries have been ruptured; a bruise.
   EXAMPLE: The contusion on Wayne's shoulder began to fade nine days after his accident.

4. **BACTERIOPHAGE (PRON: BAK-TEER-EE-UH-FAYJ):**

a virus which parasitises a bacterium by infecting and reproducing inside it.

EXAMPLE: A rare bacteriophage was detected in the patient during a routine check.

5. **LITURGICAL (PRON: LI-TUH-JIK-UHL):**

relating to liturgy or worship.

EXAMPLE: The priest donned his liturgical vestments and walked to the cathedral.

COMPREHENSION

Pick the correct definition of the following words:

1. **PARAGOGE (PRON: PARA-GOH-JEE)**

   a) On holiday in China, we climbed one hundred steps to reach the paragoge.

   b) Read this passage and note down a paragoge, instructed the teacher.

   c) Louis took his paragoge to the vet because it had no appetite.

2. **TUSSOCK (PRON: TUHS-UHK)**

   a) The golf ball was eventually found hidden in a tussock near the putting green.

   b) The vicar wears a special tussock at Easter services.

   c) Although the tussock is larger, it is often mistaken for a frog.

3. **FRICATIVE (PRON: FRIK-UH-TIV)**

   a) The speech therapist demonstrated the fricative sounds made by certain letters.

   b) When launching a ship, the fricative is usually a bottle of champagne.

   c) The fricative haircut is currently the most popular for fashion-conscious boys.

4. **CYNOSURE (PRON: SIN-AZURE)**

   a) As she stepped out of the limousine, the princess was the cynosure for the waiting crowd.

   b) In the Middle Ages, farmers used a cynosure to harvest the wheat.

   c) Cynosure clouds mean rain is not far away.

5. **FURFURACEOUS (PRON: FUR-FURE-RAY-SHUHS)**

   a) The furfuraceous ride is the most daring in the fairground.

   b) As its name suggests, the furfuraceous sofa is covered in fur.

   c) Darren's furfuraceous skin had the doctor puzzled.

MENTAL MATHS

MULTIPLICATION

1.   435.2 x 8 =

2.   852.5 x 9 =

3.   724.5 x 7 =

ADDITION

1.   17 + 98 + 63 + 93 =

2.   55 + 37 + 13 + 35 =

3.   16 + 31 + 61 + 41 =

SUBTRACTION

1.   965 - 93.9 =

2.   669 - 92.8 =

3.   988 - 99.4 =

DIVISION

1. $43.8 \div 6 = 7.3$
2. $91.7 \div 7 = 13.1$
3. $38.8 \div 4 = 9.7$

MIXED CALCULATIONS

1. $20 \times 2 - 18 \times 7 = 154$
2. $11 \times 5 - 16 \times 5 = 195$
3. $17 \times 3 - 15 \times 3 = 108$

MENSA CHALLENGE

1. Spine is to back as stomach is to:
    a) top
    b) bottom
    c) front

2. If A = 1, B = 2, C = 3 and so on, what is the total value of the word WIT?

3. What is the missing number? 97, 90, 83, ?, 69, 62

4. A shop gives a £20 voucher in exchange for 4,000 points. In pounds, what is the voucher value of 1,200 points?

5.   How many squares can you see?

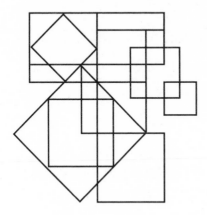

6.   Add one letter to complete one word and start the other:
     OBO (...) AST

7.   How many more 5s are in the box than 2s?

1	3	66	2	7	0	1	3
7	5	3	8	11	5	3	8
66	7	11	7	0	6	8	7
3	8	7	1	8	77	5	11
7	3	5	77	2	0	66	0

8.   What is the missing number? 50, 52, 56, ?, 70, 80

9.   Of 24 decorations, half are gold, one third are silver, and
     the remainder are red. Nine gold are used. How many
     gold and silver decorations remain?

10. How many triangles can you see?

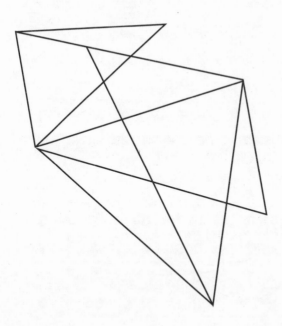

HISTORY

1. The UK fought with which other country over sovereignty of the Falkland Islands?

2. The philosopher Anaximander said that the Earth was the shape of which musical instrument?

3. Which politician was dominant in Athens between 443 and 429BC?

4. With the initials AV, in which voting system do citizens number the candidates in order of preference on the ballot paper?

5. Which city-state's king, Tarquin the Proud, was ousted in 509BC?

6.   In the late 18th century, Saint Domingue was the French territory on the island of Hispaniola – what was the Spanish half called?

7.   Which emperor of Japan died in January 1989?

8.   In the play *Alcestis*, which Greek hero rescues Alcestis from the Underworld?

9.   Under the democratic system, what Greek word was used for Athens's ten military commanders?

10. Zeno and Parmenides were part of which philosophical school, based in Italy?

GENERAL KNOWLEDGE

1. What is the name of Africa's longest river?

2. What nationality is the composer Richard Wagner?

3. In which US state is the Space Center at Cape Canaveral?

4. What is the capital city of the Czech Republic?

5. In which European country would you find the active volcano Vesuvius?

6. Which British physician introduced the smallpox vaccine to Britain in 1796 after his experiment on eight-year-old James Phipps?

7. 2013 is the Year of the Snake, but how many animals are there in the Chinese calendar?

8. Its capital is Sofia, but what is the name of this European country?

9. Which English naturalist first proposed the theory of evolution by natural selection?

10. The Soviet Union launched the first man-made satellite to orbit the Earth in 1957, but what was its name?

11. Chalk, siltstone and limestone are classified as which type of rock?

12. Which freshwater lake in North America is the largest by surface area of any lake in the world?

13. Which chemical element is the most abundant in the Sun?

14. How many official languages does South Africa have?

15.   What is the name of either of the two largest optical telescopes situated on an extinct volcano in Hawaii?

SCIENCE

1. How many leaflets grow from the same point in a trifoliate plant?

2. If an SI unit is preceded by centi-, as in centimetre, how many times smaller than the basic unit is it?

3. The Long March rocket was a launch vehicle built by which country?

4. The number of particles in one mole of any substance is named after whom?

5. The plasmalemma is another name for which part of a cell?

6. The reaction which breaks large alkanes into smaller alkanes and alkenes is called what?

7. Two electrically charged particles will attract if their charges are what?

8. What effect does a decrease in pressure have on a liquid's boiling point?

9. Lavoisier's theory that matter can neither be created nor destroyed in a chemical reaction is known by what name?

10. On the celestial sphere, positions to the north or south of the celestial equator are given by lines of what?

ADVANCED LANGUAGE

Solve the following five anagrams:

1. **m e p g h l**

   The mucus secreted by the walls of the respiratory tract.

2. **s p y l o o p h i h**

   The study or creation of theories about basic things such as the nature of existence, knowledge and thought, or about how people should live.

3. **p a n t e r c a n r y s**

   The quality that an object or substance has when you can see through it.

4. **t o p t u r i e e**

   A movement in ballet dancing.

5. **t a p e r p i n p i r a o**

   Not useful or suitable for a particular situation.

SUDDEN DEATH

30% of 450 =

ANSWERS

COMPREHENSION

1. b) Read this passage and note down a paragoge, instructed the teacher.

   DEF: the addition of a letter or syllable to a word in particular contexts or as a language develops. For example, *st* in *amongst*.

2. a) The golf ball was eventually found hidden in a tussock near the putting green.

   DEF: a small area of grass that is thicker or longer than the grass growing around it.

3. a) The speech therapist demonstrated the fricative sounds made by certain letters.

   DEF: denoting a type of consonant made by the friction of breath in a narrow opening, producing a turbulent air flow.

4. a) As she stepped out of the limousine, the princess was the cynosure for the waiting crowd.

DEF: A person or thing that is the centre of attention or admiration.

5. c) Darren's furfuraceous skin had the doctor puzzled.
    DEF: covered with or characterised by scales that resemble bran.

MENTAL MATHS
Multiplication
1. 3481.6
2. 7672.5
3. 5071.5

Addition
1. 271
2. 140
3. 149

Subtraction
1. 871.1
2. 576.2
3. 888.6

Division

1. 7.3
2. 13.1
3. 9.7

Mixed Calculations

1. 154
2. 195
3. 108

MENSA CHALLENGE

1. c) Front
2. 52
3. 76
4. £6 (20 (4000); 10 (2000), therefore 1200 ÷ 200 = 6)
5. 19
6. OBO (E) AST / OBO (L) AST
7. 2 (5 x 4; 2 x 2)
8. 62
9. 11 (24 decorations; 12 - 9 = 3 + 8 = 11)
10. 21

HISTORY

1.   Argentina
2.   Drum
3.   Pericles
4.   Alternative vote
5.   Rome
6.   Santo Domingo
7.   Hirohito (ACCEPT: Sh wa)
8.   Heracles (ACCEPT: Hercules)
9.   Strategoi (ACCEPT: strategos)
10. Eleatic School

GENERAL KNOWLEDGE

1.   Nile
2.   German
3.   Florida
4.   Prague
5.   Italy
6.   Edward Jenner
7.   12

8. Bulgaria
9. Charles Darwin
10. Sputnik 1 (ACCEPT: Sputnik)
11. Sedimentary
12. Lake Superior
13. Hydrogen
14. Eleven
15. Keck I or Keck II (ACCEPT: Keck)

SCIENCE

1. Three
2. 100
3. China
4. Amadeo Avogadro
5. Cell membrane(ACCEPT: plasma membrane/ cytoplasmic membrane)
6. Cracking
7. Opposite
8. Decreases it (ACCEPT: decrease)
9. Law of conservation of mass
10. Declination

ADVANCED LANGUAGE

1. phlegm
2. philosophy
3. transparency
4. pirouette
5. inappropriate

SUDDEN DEATH

135

♀ Did You Know? ♀

How to Control Your Nerves and Keep Cool

Learning to control our nerves is a life skill and important when it comes to revising, exam situations, interviews and high-stress environments. Feeling anxious can block us retaining information or retrieving it when we need it most. It is incredibly common, no matter our age, background and overall confidence.

It sounds obvious to say that **sleep**, **good diet**, **exercise** and drinking plenty of **water** help – but they really do. These are things that we often forget when we are working hard and do not feel we have time to stop. If we don't look after ourselves properly, then our brains will not respond in the way we want them to.

Know your subject. Anxiety tends to come when we know we haven't put in the effort required and there are gaps in our understanding. Being underprepared for anything is often a mistake, but more particularly when it comes to exams and interviews. Don't put yourself in that position and give yourself enough time and space to prepare.

Positive mental attitude is a must. As soon as we begin to doubt ourselves, the intricate map of knowledge and self-assurance we have built up will start to wobble. It is good to be sure of our ability without being overconfident or rushing ahead without thought. We can catch ourselves making comparisons to others and measuring our achievements against our peers'. A little healthy competition is a good thing, but we need to stay on our own course and not let it affect the choices we make.

There are various ways to achieve calm, whether through **deep-breathing** exercises, **meditation**, **visualisation** or talking yourself through something. It is easy to feel overwhelmed by the task in hand or rush into it, so take a moment to quietly consider before tackling the situation. Focusing on an image is a powerful support tool, whether it is a pet, a favourite view or a treat you are heading home to. If you can teach yourself how to be calm under pressure, you can be cool for life.

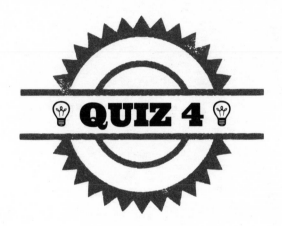

SPELLING

Spell the following five words:

1. **LAMINECTOMY (PRON: LAM-MIN-NECK-TOMY):**
    a surgical operation to remove the back of one or more
    vertebrae, usually to give access to the spinal cord or to
    relieve pressure on the nerves.
    EXAMPLE: Mary was relieved when her dad's
    laminectomy operation went ahead, as he was in a great
    deal of pain.

2. **MAGNILOQUENT (PRON: MAG-NIL-O-QUENT):**
    using high-flown or bombastic language.
    EXAMPLE: The English professor used very pompous
    and magniloquent sentences in his tutorial, much to the
    student's disgust.

3. **BALNEOTHERAPY (PRON: BAL-NEO-THERAPY):**

    the treatment of disease by bathing in mineral springs

    EXAMPLE: The health spa offers a range of treatments, from manicures and facials to massages and balneotherapy.

4. **GLYCOPROTEIN (PRON: GLY-CO-PROTEIN):**

    in biochemistry, any of a class of proteins which have carbohydrate groups attached to the polypeptide chain.

    EXAMPLE: The scientist analysed the string of glycoprotein in the petri dish.

5. **PLEIAD (PRON: PLY-UHD):**

    an outstanding group of seven people or things.

    EXAMPLE: The maestro named a pleiad of pianists who were once his pupils.

COMPREHENSION

Pick the correct definition of the following words:

1. **NEOPRENE (PRON: NEE-UH-PREEN)**

   a) The cinema was visible from a distance, thanks to the neoprene sign above the door.

   b) The worst part of scuba diving was getting in and out of the skin-tight neoprene suit.

   c) At the dog-grooming salon, Jessica's job was to neoprene the dogs' coats.

2. **REVENANT (PRON: REV-UH-NUHNT)**

   a) It is important to keep a close eye on a company's revenant and finances.

   b) Mollie's grandma had to cover her eyes each time the revenant appeared in the horror film.

   c) It was a revenant throw which sent the crowd wild and put John in the final.

3. **TULSI (PRON: TOOL-SEE)**

   a) The skipper of the yacht taught the sailors how to tie a tulsi.

   b) Eddie dressed up as a tulsi for Halloween.

   c) Sudip hoped the Indian medicine containing tulsi would cure him.

4. **ORTHOGONAL (PRON: ORTHOG-GON-AL)**

   a) Once Rita had seen the orthogonal nurse, her feet would feel much better.

   b) An orthogonal is a snake which has a venomous bite.

   c) The children loved to make an orthogonal pattern using their squares and rectangles.

5. **NARTHEX (PRON: NAR-THEX)**

   a) How Jim gets a whole model ship through the narthex of a bottle, is still a mystery.

   b) It was a good idea to use the narthex as a play area for the church toddler group.

   c) Once the fence was erected, John had to paint it with narthex.

MENTAL MATHS

MULTIPLICATION

1. $494.7 \times 6 =$

2. $969.1 \times 5 =$

3. $944.3 \times 5 =$

ADDITION

1. $55 + 15 + 89 + 15 + 26 + 77 =$

2. $86 + 55 + 99 + 13 + 14 + 33 =$

3. $78 + 60 + 95 + 46 + 92 + 94 =$

SUBTRACTION

1. $786 - 90.2 =$

2. $996 - 94.2 =$

3. $885 - 65.5 =$

DIVISION

1. $92.4 \div 7 =$
2. $22.8 \div 3 =$
3. $43.2 \div 3 =$

MIXED CALCULATIONS

1. $17 \times 5 - 19 \times 4 =$
2. $15 \times 6 - 20 \times 4 =$
3. $11 \times 3 - 15 \times 7 =$

MENSA CHALLENGE

1. Dusk is to evening as dawn is to:

    a) night

    b) noon

    c) morning

2. How many more 9s are there than 0s?

2	8	5	9	7	2	8	5
1	9	6	4	5	0	7	9
4	22	0	2	9	1	4	11
9	1	3	8	7	5	9	0
5	6	9	1	4	0	6	33

3. What is the next number? 1024, 64, 16, 4, 4, ?

4. Cards cost 42p individually or £3.50 for a pack of 10.
    In pounds and pence, how much cheaper is it to buy 2
    packs of cards rather than 20 individual cards?

5. How many squares can you see?

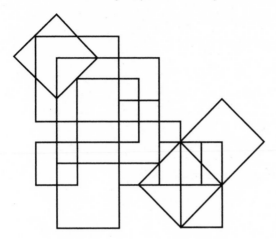

6. Add one letter to complete one word and start the other:

POL (...) PEN

7. If A = 1, B = 2, C = 3 and so on, what is the total value of the word COW?

8. What is the missing number?

6, 8, 14, ?, 36, 58

9. A cyclist covers 56km in four hours. In kilometres, what distance does he travel in two and a half hours?

10. How many triangles can you see?

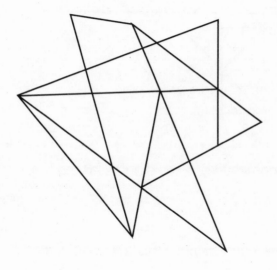

HISTORY

1. In 1791, the Brandenburg Gate was completed in which German city?

2. The sculpture *Discobolus*, by Myron, shows a man doing what?

3. In Victorian times, the example name on a British soldier's new recruit form was Thomas what?

4. The last Soviet troops left which country in February 1989?

5. A political party's list of policies that it promises to carry out if elected is known as what?

6. The first voyage of the steamship the *Great Western* was from Bristol to which American city?

7.   Which revolutionary leader was assassinated in Mexico
     on 10 April 1919?

8.   Which province of Serbia did Slobodan Milosevic strip of
     its autonomy on becoming president?

9.   The first trip organised by Thomas Cook was a one-day
     outing from Leicester to where?

10. Between 1801 and 1901, the percentage of the working
     population employed in farming dropped from 32 per
     cent to what?

GENERAL KNOWLEDGE

1. What is the name of the ancient Egyptian writing that is made up of pictograms?

2. What is the largest continent in the world?

3. Which famous battle ended in the defeat of Harold II of England by William, Duke of Normandy in 1066?

4. What is the name of the South American country whose capital is Santiago?

5. Which planet is closest to the Sun?

6. What is the name of the Hindu Festival of Lights?

7. In which country would you find the world's longest railway bridge, which opened in 2011 and runs for 164km?

8. Which Greek mathematician and inventor is famous for defining the principle of the lever?

9. The mechanical printing press was invented by Johannes Gutenberg, but what nationality was he?

10. In which year did some women in the UK win the right to vote for the first time?

11. Which artist developed a painting technique called pointillism?

12. Which Latin term is used to describe the stiffening of a body usually occurring two to eight hours after death?

13. Its capital is Montevideo, but what is the name of this South American country?

14. In which section of an orchestra would you find drums and cymbals?

15.   In which year was the Battle of Britain?

SCIENCE

1. In taxonomy, the names of species are given in which language?

2. In the binomial system used in taxonomy, how many words make up the names given to each living organism?

3. What is the collective name given to 12 out of the 13 constellations on the Sun's path along the ecliptic?

4. What name is given to a substance with molecules formed from the combination of three molecules of a monomer?

5. What name is given to the equal and opposite forces which decrease the length of an object?

6.   What name is given to the trapping of solar energy by atmospheric carbon dioxide?

7.   Which animal phylum is characterised by segmented bodies, jointed legs and a hard exoskeleton?

8.   Which cellulose structure is present in plant cells, but not animal cells?

9.   Rapid flashes of phosphorescent light are known as what?

10.   The candela is the SI unit used to measure what?

ADVANCED LANGUAGE

Solve the following five anagrams:

1. **g r a p o a n**

    a model or pattern of perfection or excellence.

2. **l e s d i e b f n e**

    capable of being defended, as in war, an argument, etc.

3. **t h s i n s e y s**

    the combination of elements into a whole.

4. **o n t o r i e a n t i**

    position or positioning with relation to the points of the
    compass or other specific directions.

5. **m y t h e h a p o r l**

    an abnormally low body temperature, as induced in
    elderly people by exposure to cold weather.

SUDDEN DEATH

Calculate: 30% of 600

ANSWERS

COMPREHENSION

1.   b) The worst part of scuba diving was getting in and out of the skin-tight neoprene suit.
     DEF: neoprene, noun, a synthetic polymer resembling rubber, resistant to oil, heat and weathering.

2.   b) Mollie's grandma had to cover her eyes each time the revenant appeared in the horror film.
     DEF: a person who has returned, especially supposedly from the dead.

3.   c) Sudip hoped the Indian medicine containing tulsi would cure him.
     DEF: a kind of basil which is cultivated by Hindus as a sacred plant. Tulsi is widely used as a medicinal herbal tea.

4.   c) The children loved to make an orthogonal pattern using squares and rectangles.
     DEF: of or involving right angles or at right angles.

5. b) It was a good idea to use the narthex as a play area for the church toddler group.

    DEF: an antechamber, porch or distinct area at the western entrance of some early Christian churches, separated off by a railing.

MENTAL MATHS
Multiplication
1. 2968.2
2. 4845.5
3. 4721.5

Addition
1. 277
2. 300
3. 465

Subtraction
1. 695.8
2. 901.8
3. 819.5

Division

1. 13.2
2. 7.6
3. 14.4

Mixed Calculations

1. 264
2. 280
3. 126

MENSA CHALLENGE

1. Morning
2. 3
3. 1
4. £1.40 (2 packs £7.00 (0.42 x 20 = 8.40; 840 - 7.00 = 1.40)
5. 25
6. POL (O) PEN

    NB: POLS/SPEN. One in this pair is found in Oxford Online, but not in the *Oxford English Dictionary*, so would therefore not be allowed.
7. 41.3 + 15 + 23 = 41

8.   22

9.   35km (56 ÷ 4 = 14 (2 x 14 = 28 + 7 = 35)

10.   24

HISTORY

1.   Berlin

2.   Throwing a discus (ACCEPT: preparing to throw a discus)

3.   Atkins

4.   Afghanistan

5.   Manifesto

6.   New York City

7.   Emiliano Zapata

8.   Kosovo (ACCEPT: Vojvodina)

9.   Loughborough

10.   6%

GENERAL KNOWLEDGE

1.   Hieroglyphics

2.   Asia

3. Battle of Hastings

4. Chile

5. Mercury

6. Diwali

7. China

8. Archimedes

9. German

10. 1918

11. Georges Seurat

12. Rigor mortis (DO NOT ACCEPT: rigor)

13. Uruguay

14. Percussion

15. 1940

SCIENCE

1. Latin

2. Two

3. Signs of the Zodiac

4. Trimer

5. Compression

6. Greenhouse effect

7. Arthropods

8. Cell wall

9. Scintillations

10. Luminous intensity (ACCEPT: intensity of light)

ADVANCED LANGUAGE

1. Paragon

2. Defensible

3. Synthesis

4. Orientation

5. Hypothermia

SUDDEN DEATH

180

♀ Did You Know? ♀

Why Sleep is More Important Than Diet and Exercise

The powerful triangle of good diet, regular exercise and a decent night's sleep is key to our wellbeing. We need the balanced combination of all three to engender a fit, happy lifestyle and give us the strength to deal with any challenges and pressures we may face.

Interestingly, however, it turns out that sleep is just that little bit more important than the other two. Without the right amount of rest, we find it harder to function effectively, and this then impacts on our ability to exercise and make good food choices. Sleep is also crucial to the state of our mental health, helping us to concentrate, make decisions and enable us to retain information.

So what happens if we do not get enough sleep? One or two nights shouldn't make a difference, although we may feel a little tired during the day. It's a lack of sleep over a prolonged period that will create problems. It affects our hormones, immune system (which can make us more prone to illness) and induces depression and anxiety. Tiredness causes

our metabolism to slow down and we battle with lethargy throughout the day, craving foods high in sugar to give us instant cheap energy. It's an easy cycle to get caught in, but a dangerous one.

We need to give sleep the respect it deserves and measure it in quality, not just quantity. Whilst our bodies rest, our minds are active, ordering and storing what we have learnt during the day and renewing our memories. These are essential hours for us.

If you struggle at bedtime, consider changing or establishing a routine to help. It has been proven that we sleep better if we go to bed and wake up at the same time each day. Environment also plays its part, so make sure your bedroom is a quiet, cool, dark sanctuary after a busy day. Daily exercise, a reduced caffeine intake, an early supper and a bath before we turn in are all good elements to incorporate into your daily regime. Don't be tempted to use your phone as an alarm – invest in an actual alarm clock – and don't take your phone to bed. Take a book instead!

QUIZ 5

QUIZ 5

SPELLING

Spell the following five words:

1.   **VAINGLORIOUS (PRON: VAIN-GLOR-REE-US):**
     characterised by excessive vanity.
     EXAMPLE: The chef's vainglorious ways were often
     blamed for high turnover amongst her staff.

2.   **PUGNACIOUS (PRON: PUG-NAY-SHUSS):**
     eager or quick to argue, quarrel or fight.
     EXAMPLE: The adult males are extremely pugnacious
     and fight fiercely with one another.

3.   **MEGATHERIUM (PRON: MEGA-THEER-RIUM):**
     an extinct giant ground sloth of the Pliocene and
     Pleistocene epochs in America, reaching a height of 5m
     (16ft) when standing erect.

EXAMPLE: Megatherium was one of the largest mammals known, weighing up to eight tons, about as much as an African bull elephant.

4. **DIAPHORESIS (PRON: DYE-A-FA-REE-SISS):**
a technical name for sweating.
EXAMPLE: Many medical conditions can cause diaphoresis.

5. **MACHISMO (PRON: MA-KIZ-MOH):**
exaggerated masculine pride.
EXAMPLE: He has to prove his machismo by going on the scariest rides.

COMPREHENSION

Pick the correct definition of the following words:

1. **ATELIER (PRON: UH-TEL-YA)**
   a) Arriving at the painter's atelier, Lucy immediately fell in love with the portrait of her son.
   b) The atelier told the porter to take the guests' luggage to their room.
   c) Stuart wondered if he should atelier the soup before or after it was cooked.

2. **ADJUNCT (PRON: AD-JUNKT)**
   a) Being the school adjunct is a position to be proud of.
   b) The media course is an adjunct to the main degree course.
   c) Kerry used the adjunct in her house to store all her boxes of photographs.

3.   NAUTILUS (PRON: NAWT-TILL-LUS)

a) The spiral shell of the nautilus looked beautiful to Shireen.

b) The nautilus is the central part of a church building.

c) A nautilus child will be punished, warned the headmaster.

4.   PARQUETRY (PRON: PAR-KET-TREE)

a) The parquetry is a trumpet solo piece of considerable length and difficulty.

b) Hazel bought her mum a box of her favourite rose parquetry for Mother's Day.

c) The parquetry furniture on display throughout the house is what made Belle and Ted want to buy it.

5.   EXCORIATE (PRON: EX-SCORE-REE-ATE)

a) Julie asked her mum not to excoriate her toast.

b) The student teacher was told that it is not good practice to excoriate the pupils.

c) Mark was not impressed with his last score and would like to excoriate it.

MENTAL MATHS

MULTIPLICATION
1. 625.2 x 9 = 5626.8
2. 819.5 x 9 = 7375.5
3. 752.8 x 5 = 3764

ADDITION
1. 30 + 62 + 25 + 13 + 25 + 27 =
2. 49 + 14 + 26 + 19 + 38 + 11 =
3. 66 + 91 + 76 + 27 + 92 + 49 =

SUBTRACTION
1. 852 - 93.2 =
2. 728 - 72.7 =
3. 861 - 72.4 =

DIVISION

1. $78.4 \div 7 =$
2. $27.6 \div 3 =$
3. $25.8 \div 3 =$

MIXED CALCULATIONS

1. $28 \times 6 - 14 \times 8 \div 7 =$
2. $17 \times 6 - 17 \times 2 \div 5 =$
3. $22 \times 5 - 25 \times 3 \div 5 =$

MENSA CHALLENGE

1.   Add one letter to complete one word and start the other:
      PIN (...) DGE

2.   If A = 1, B = 2, C = 3 and so on, what is the total value
      of the word FRY?

3.   What is the missing number? 96, 88, 80, ?, 64, 56

4.   A cleaning liquid must be diluted 1 part cleaner to 7
      parts of water. In millilitres, how much cleaner will be
      needed to make 1.6 litres of solution?

5.   How many squares can you see?

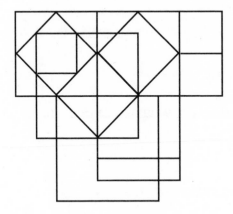

6.   Buy is to bought as bring is to:

a) fetch

b) obtained

c) brought

7.   How many more 1s are there than 6s?

5	1	2	6	1	3	5	4
7	8	1	5	4	7	1	6
5	4	6	1	5	1	7	9
1	2	4	22	1	6	88	1
9	6	1	2	3	5	1	6

8.   What is the next number? 225, 196, 169, 144, 121, ?

9.   A cleaner is paid £72 for 8 hours' work. In pounds, how much do they earn for 20 hours' work?

10.   How many triangles can you see?

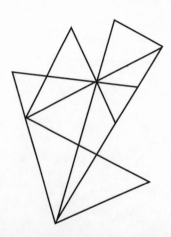

HISTORY

1. Which famous underwater explorer died on 25 June 1997?

2. Which Roman statesman, who died in 43BC, is considered the father of constitutionalism?

3. What did France abolish on 4 February 1794?

4. Which American city hosted the 1996 Summer Olympics?

5. On 14 August 1790, the Treaty of Värälä ended a war between Russia and which country?

6. Which Greek mathematician, who lived around 300BC, wrote a book called *Elements*?

7. In 1996, Madeleine Albright became the first American woman to be nominated to what position?

8. The American Eli Whitney invented which machine in 1793?

9. In June 1989, which trade-union movement won a majority in the Polish elections?

10. In the French Revolutionary calendar, how long did each month last?

GENERAL KNOWLEDGE

1. Hollywood is a district within which American city?

2. 'Richard Of York Gave Battle In Vain' is the phrase used to remember the colours of the visible spectrum. What colour does the word 'Battle' represent?

3. From which country does the musical instrument the didgeridoo originate?

4. How is Mount Godwin Austen, the world's second-highest mountain, better known?

5. Its capital is Budapest, but what is the name of this landlocked European country?

6. Born in 1996, what was the name of the first mammal to be cloned from an adult cell?

7. What is the name of the first real space tourist who paid $20 million for a week on board the *International Space Station* in 2001?

8. Which iconic building in Sydney, Australia is described as organic architecture, with its curved shapes inspired by nature?

9. What name is used to describe the film industry based in Mumbai, India?

10. Roald Amundsen reached the North Pole in December 1911, but what was his nationality?

11. What is the name of the telescope that replaced the Hubble Space telescope in 2013?

12. At sea level, what is the temperature in Fahrenheit of liquid water heated to boiling point?

13. On which island in Thailand would you find the 15-metre-tall landmark 'The Big Buddha', which was built in 1972?

14. In which year did the Berlin Wall come down?

15. What is the number of the last manned Apollo mission to the Moon in 1972?

SCIENCE

1.   In which state do a substance's shape and volume remain constant?

2.   Locations on the Earth's surface can be described using two coordinates: longitude and which other?

3.   Which craft orbited Jupiter between 1995 and 2003?

4.   Which metal has the chemical symbol W?

5.   With the symbol G, what is the four-letter prefix which means 10 to the power of 9?

6.   The catalyst used in the contact process to make sulphuric acid is Vanadium what?

7.   The coefficient of friction, mu, is the ratio of frictional force to which other force?

8. The Earth's axis is currently tilted by how many degrees, to within one degree?

9. The law of constant composition was developed in the late 18th century by which Frenchman?

10. The number of sunspots visible on the Sun varies according to a cycle that lasts approximately how long?

ADVANCED LANGUAGE

Solve the following five anagrams:

1. **g l u e r o n o y**

   The study of the structure, function and diseases of the nervous system.

2. **i o n r i g n e l e a**

   A member of certain military forces or associations.

3. **d i n b u s c e s e**

   The gradual sinking of landforms to a lower level as a result of earth movements, mining operations and so on.

4. **p o n y a r c h a g e o**

   The scientific study of sea currents, the sea bed and the fish and animals that live in the sea.

5. **c l o u r f e t e n s**

   Producing light when acted upon by radiant energy.

SUDDEN DEATH

30% of 500 =

ANSWERS

COMPREHENSION

1. a) Arriving at the painter's atelier, Lucy immediately fell in love with the portrait of her son.
    DEF: a workshop or studio, especially one used by an artist or designer.

2. b) The media course is an adjunct to the main degree course.
    DEF: a thing added to something else as a supplementary rather than an essential part.

3. a) The spiral shell of the nautilus looked beautiful to Shireen.
    DEF: a cephalopod mollusc with a light external spiral shell and numerous short tentacles around the mouth.

4. c) The parquetry furniture on display throughout the house is what made Belle and Ted want to buy it.

DEF: inlaid work of blocks of various woods arranged in a geometric pattern, esp for flooring or furniture.

5.   b) The student teacher was told that it is not good practice to excoriate the pupils.
DEF: criticize (someone) severely.

MENTAL MATHS
Multiplication
1.   5626.8
2.   7375.5
3.   3764

Addition
1.   182
2.   157
3.   401

Subtraction
1.   758.8
2.   655.3
3.   788.6

Division

1. 11.2

2. 9.2

3. 8.6

Mixed Calculations

1. 176

2. 34

3. 51

MENSA CHALLENGE

1. PIN (E) DGE

2. NB: PINA/ADGE. One in this pair is found in Oxford Online, but not in the *Oxford English Dictionary*, so would therefore not be allowed.

3. 49 (6 + 18 + 25 = 49)

4. 72

5. 200ml (1600 ÷ 8 = 200)

6. 16

7. Brought

8. 5

9.   100
10. £180 (72 ÷ 8 = 9, 9 x 20 = 180)
11. 26

HISTORY

1.   Jacques Cousteau

2.   Marcus Cicero (ACCEPT: Marcus Tullius Cicero/Tully)

3.   Slavery

4.   Atlanta

5.   Sweden

6.   Euclid

7.   Secretary of State (NB: nominated in December; sworn
     in January 1997)

8.   Cotton gin

9.   Solidarity (ACCEPT: Solidarnose)

10. 30 days

GENERAL KNOWLEDGE

1. Los Angeles (ACCEPT: LA)
2. Blue
3. Australia
4. K2 (ACCEPT: Dapsang)
5. Hungary
6. Dolly
7. Dennis Tito
8. Sydney Opera House (ACCEPT: Opera House)
9. Bollywood
10. Norwegian
11. James Webb Space Telescope (ACCEPT: JWST)
12. 212°F
13. Koh Samui
14. 1989
15. Apollo 17 (ACCEPT: 17)

SCIENCE

1. Solid (NB: When not heated, or cut or whatever)
2. Latitude

3. Galileo (NB: it launched in 1989, but began orbiting Jupiter in 1995)

4. Tungsten

5. [10 Billion] GIGA

6. Pentoxide

7. Normal Contact Force (ACCEPT: normal force)

8. 23.4 degrees (ACCEPT: from 22.4 to 24.5 degrees; Nasa has it currently at 23.5.)

9. Joseph Proust

10. Eleven years

ADVANCED LANGUAGE

1. neurology

2. legionnaire

3. subsidence

4. oceanography

5. fluorescent

SUDDEN DEATH

150

♀ Did You Know? ♀

Brain Food

We are what we eat. This is just as true for the brain as it is for the rest of the body. Good nutrition is key in keeping our grey matter healthy and functioning to its best ability which, in turn, benefits our general wellbeing. There is still much to learn about the relationship between what we eat and the effects it has on us mentally, but there are four areas that can be directly linked.

Whilst we naturally produce protective molecules known as antioxidants, we also rely on our diets to create more of them to give us energy and help us fight brain disease. Good fats, vitamins and minerals are high in antioxidants, so our

diet should be rich in these food groups, which include green leafy vegetables (like kale and spinach) and berries (blueberries are the highest in antioxidants). Beetroot is thought to be full of cancer-protecting antioxidants and boosts blood to the brain.

Essential fatty acids can help with improving synapse brain pathways and memory, but cannot be made by the body, so anything containing omega-3 fats such as oily fish (wild salmon, mackerel and sardines) is recommended. Choosing pumpkin seeds (which are also rich in zinc) or walnuts as a snack is ideal, as they are thought to encourage memory skills and a happy mood.

The neurotransmitters responsible for concentration, learning, memory, the immune and nervous systems operate well when fed with protein-inspired amino acids. Meat, dairy products and eggs all contain amino acids, as well as less obvious ingredients like watercress, seeds, avocados (the fruit lowest in sugar, but highest in protein) and quinoa.

The brain gets much needed energy from glucose-rich foods that provide steady, slow-release energy, rather than an instant high followed by a big slump later in the day. Choose brown rice, pasta and bread over any of their wayward white versions. Avoiding processed food generally is good advice, as it does not supply the brilliant vitamins and minerals that fresh produce does. Instead, focus on vitamin B (6,12 and folic) to preserve against cognitive issues, vitamin C (blackcurrants, red peppers and citrus) to increase mental agility and vitamin E (leafy green veg, nuts, seeds, wholegrains, eggs) to enhance brain performance.

And the great news is that we can include dark chocolate on our good-foods list, as it is believed to be anti-inflammatory!

QUIZ 6

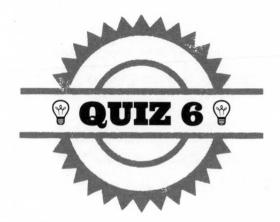

SPELLING

Spell the following five words:

1. **PYROXENITE (PRON: PIE-ROCKS-IN-NATE):**
   a dark, greenish, granular, intrusive igneous rock
   consisting chiefly of pyroxenes and olivine.
   EXAMPLE: Jack was delighted when he added
   pyroxenite to his rock collection.

2. **CATECHETICS (PRON: KAT-A-KET-IKS):**
   religious teaching by means of spoken questions and
   answers.
   EXAMPLE: The century witnessed a revival in
   catechetics.

3. **QUIXOTIC (PRON: QUIX-OTT-ICK):**
   extremely idealistic; unrealistic and impractical.
   EXAMPLE: This is a vast, exciting and, some say,
   quixotic project.

4. **SAURISCHIAN (PRON: SAW-RISK-EE-AN):**
    of an order of dinosaurs that includes the theropods and sauropods.
    EXAMPLE: The saurischian dinosaurs were the ancestors of birds.

5. **CONCINNITY (PRON: KUN-SIN-I-TEE):**
    a successful arrangement of parts so that they all fit well together.
    EXAMPLE: Architects imitate the concinnity seen in nature.

COMPREHENSION

Pick the correct definition of the following words:

1. **SOMNAMBULISM (PRON: SOM-NAM-BYOO-LIS-EM)**
   a) To be able to do somnambulism effectively you must use the correct paintbrush.
   b) Before unpacking for the sleepover, Amanda told her friend about her somnambulism.
   c) Dave's brush with a jellyfish caused a somnambulism that had to be treated immediately.

2. **GNOMON (PRON: NOH-MON)**
   a) The gnomon circled the air before pouncing on its prey.
   b) Scouts are taught to tell the time using a gnomon on the sundial.
   c) Gnomon dancing is very common amongst tribes in the Amazon.

3.   FEBRIFUGE (PRON: FEB-RI-FYOOH-J)

a) Doctors usually give patients a febrifuge when their temperature is too high.

b) If you don't put febrifuge into your car engine in winter, it will freeze.

c) Living in the heart of the countryside, it is essential to have a febrifuge in case the electricity fails.

4.   DENTICULATE (PRON: DEN-TICK-YOU-LATE)

a) The denticulate knitting of the baby's shawl was greatly admired.

b) The guest speaker was very denticulate and interesting.

c) Mary loved the denticulate shell she had found on the beach.

5.   BICEPHALOUS (PRON: BYE-CEFA-LOSS)

a) Eric loved to be completely alone, flying his bicephalous.

b) Mia didn't like her big brother's toys, especially the bicephalous warrior.

c) Mum and her friends held a bicephalous coffee morning for charity.

MENTAL MATHS

MULTIPLICATION

1.   779.1 x 5 =

2.   972.6 x 9 =

3.   907.5 x 9 =

ADDITION

1.   97 + 22 + 13 + 85 + 62 + 76 =

2.   48 + 16 + 21 + 62 + 14 + 13 =

3.   78 + 73 + 29 + 94 + 34 + 72 =

SUBTRACTION

1.   505 - 77.6 =

2.   927 - 98.1 =

3.   560 - 84.3 =

DIVISION

1. $47.1 \div 3 =$
2. $31.2 \div 3 =$
3. $77.2 \div 4 =$

MIXED CALCULATIONS

1. $14 \times 4 - 27 \times 8 \div 2 =$
2. $26 \times 7 - 10 \times 2 \div 8 =$
3. $10 \times 2 - 10 \times 4 \div 5 =$

MENSA CHALLENGE

1.   Add one letter to complete one word and start the other:
      JUD (...) ATS

2.   How many more 8s are there than 1s?

3	8	4	6	8	7	2	6
22	5	33	0	8	1	9	8
1	6	8	9	1	8	2	4
8	4	1	1	5	9	8	3
7	8	6	5	3	8	2	1

3.   What is the missing number? 4, 16, 36, ?, 100, 144

4.   A train takes 44 minutes to reach the ferry port. If the
      10.30 train leaves 8 minutes late, at what time will it
      arrive?

5. How many triangles can you see?

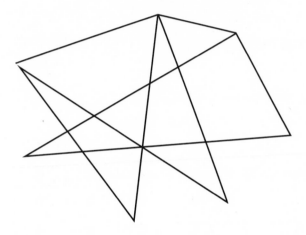

6. Feather is to chicken as scale is to:

   a) piano

   b) fish

   c) horse

7. If A = 1, B = 2, C = 3 and so on, what is the total value of the word FOX?

8. What is the next number? 144, 121, 100, 81, 64, ?

9. Petrol costs £1.50 per litre. How much, in pounds and pence, will it cost to fill a 5.5 litre can?

10. How many squares can you see?

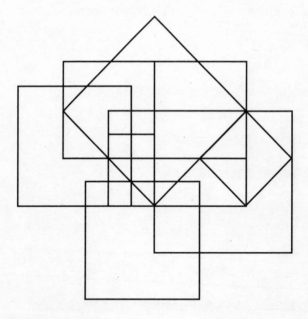

HISTORY

1.   In 1961, who was the first man to be launched into space?

2.   In June 1960, Congo gained independence from which European country?

3.   Pope Julius II summoned which artist to Rome in 1505 to create his tomb?

4.   Which word of Greek origin means 'rule by the few'?

5.   In which city in Georgia was Martin Luther King arrested in October 1960?

6.   In 1961, who became the first American to go into space?

7.   Which international protocol, regarding global warming, was signed in December 1997?

8.   What is the English name of the Moluccas, which the Portuguese explored in the early 16th century?

9.   Soldiers of which country sacked the east African city of Mombasa in 1505?

10. Which explorer claimed Florida for Spain in April 1513?

GENERAL KNOWLEDGE

1. What is the largest country in the world by area?

2. In which month of the year do Americans celebrate Thanksgiving?

3. The Tour de France is what type of race?

4. Which country's capital is called Ottawa?

5. Which is the only planet with oceans on its surface?

6. What term is used to describe a metal made by combining two or more metallic elements, especially to give greater strength or resistance to corrosion?

7. Used in forensic science, where exactly on the human body would you find ridges that form patterns of arches, loops and whorls?

8.   What is the largest moon in our solar system?

9.   In which country was the famous Battle of Waterloo fought on 18 June 1815?

10.   What is the name of the first skydiver to go faster than the speed of sound when he jumped out of a balloon 39km (24 miles) above the Earth in October 2012?

11.   What is the name of the traditional Maori dance performed by New Zealand's national rugby union team?

12.   Which term is used to describe the 19th-century artists Manet, Monet and Degas?

13.   The Twelve Apostles rock formation is situated off the coast of which country?

14.   Which composer wrote the classical music piece, *Moonlight Sonata*?

15. There are three basic types of rocks – igneous, sedimentary and which other?

SCIENCE

1. The theory that the universe began with a sudden expansion from a single point is commonly known by what name?

2. Visible light is electromagnetic radiation that can be detected by what?

3. What is the name of the force that keeps planets in orbit around a star?

4. What word is used for the speed and direction of an object?

5. Which people first used the term 'atoms' to describe tiny particles?

6. The overgrowth of aquatic plants, caused by too many nitrates, nitrites and phosphates in a river is called what?

7. What is the freezing point of water, in degrees Kelvin?

8. Which hormone is antagonistic to insulin, producing the opposite effect?

9. Which of Saturn's rings consists of microscopic ice grains coming from eruptions on the moon Enceladus?

10. Having the chemical formula HgS, which substance is the main source of mercury?

ADVANCED LANGUAGE

Solve the following five anagrams:

1. **c h i p r o y y s**

    The practice of professing standards, beliefs, etc.,
    contrary to one's real character or actual behaviour.

2. **i o n t e c e c d**

    Having a high or exaggerated opinion of oneself.

3. **h o t c r i l a r e**

    Concerned with effect or style, rather than content or
    meaning; bombastic.

4. **b e l i r e s n o r s i p**

    Not showing or done with due care for the
    consequences of one's actions or attitudes; reckless.

5. **t r a m a g e r n f y**

    Disconnected; incomplete.

SUDDEN DEATH

What is the smallest whole number that 32 and 42

will both go into?

ANSWERS

COMPREHENSION

1. b) Before unpacking for the sleepover, Amanda told her friend about her somnambulism.
    DEF: sleepwalking.

2. b) Scouts are taught to tell the time using a gnomon on the sundial.
    DEF: the projecting piece on a sundial that shows the time by the position of its shadow.

3. a) Doctors usually give patients a febrifuge when their temperature is too high.
    DEF: medicine used to reduce fever.

4. c) Mary loved the denticulate shell she had found on the beach.
    DEF: having small teeth or tooth-like projections; finely toothed.

5.   b) Mia didn't like her big brother's toys, especially the
      bicephalous warrior.
      DEF: having two heads.

MENTAL MATHS
Multiplication
1.   3895.5
2.   8753.4
3.   8167.5

Addition
1.   355
2.   174
3.   380

Subtraction
1.   427.4
2.   828.9
3.   475.7

Division
1.   15.7

2. 10.4

3. 19.3

Mixed Calculations

1. 116

2. 43

3. 8

MENSA CHALLENGE

1. JUD (O) ATS

2. 4

3. 64

4. 11.22 (1030 + 44 mins = 1114 + 8 mins delay = 11.22am)

5. 21

6. Fish

7. 45 (6 + 15 + 24 = 45)

8. 49

9. £8.25 (1.50 x 5.5 = 8.25)

10. 22

HISTORY

1. Yuri Gagarin
2. Belgium
3. Michelangelo
4. Oligarchy
5. Atlanta
6. Alan Shepard
7. Kyoto Protocol
8. Spice Islands
9. Portugal
10. Juan Ponce de León

GENERAL KNOWLEDGE

1. Russia (ACCEPT: Russian Federation; DO NOT ACCEPT: Soviet Union)
2. November
3. Cycling (ACCEPT: road cycling/bicycle race)
4. Canada
5. Earth
6. Alloy

7.   Fingerprints (ACCEPT: fingers; DO NOT ACCEPT: hands)

8.   Ganymede (ACCEPT: Jupiter III)

9.   Belgium

10. Felix Baumgartner

11. Haka

12. Impressionists (ACCEPT: Impressionism)

13. Australia

14. Beethoven

15. Metamorphic

SCIENCE

1.   Big Bang Theory

2.   Eye

3.   Gravity

4.   Velocity

5.   Greeks (ACCEPT: Ancient Greeks)

6.   Eutrophication

7.   273 (ACCEPT: 273.15/273.2)

8.   Glucagon

9.   E Ring

10. Cinnabar (ACCEPT: mercury sulphide)

ADVANCED LANGUAGE

1. hypocrisy
2. conceited
3. rhetorical
4. irresponsible
5. fragmentary

SUDDEN DEATH

672

💡 Did You Know? 💡

Give Your Brain a Break

Take a break. Long revision sessions, filled with information and fraught with stress are counterproductive to the end goal. Our brains struggle to concentrate and retain facts when we are tired, anxious and overworked. Unsurprisingly, it has been proven that taking regular scheduled breaks between study sessions helps to keep us focused on the task in hand. Just like identifying our style of working (see page 220), we also need to pinpoint the quickest way to relax.

It is always tempting to grab a coffee break, open a pack of biscuits and pick up your phone, but none of these actions nourishes you or powers you through your next block of revision. Whatever form your break takes – short and regular or longer but further apart – get outside. A breath of fresh air should be a daily ritual for us all. Spending time in nature is restorative for body and mind and reminds us of the world beyond our desks. Exercise is also a brilliant way to give the brain a rest and boost serotonin levels to aid wellbeing and memory skills. This may be a short walk around the block, a long run, a cooling swim, a yoga

session or a game of football with friends. Whatever you choose to do, it should raise your heart rate and take your mind off the study mountain you are climbing. Returning to your notes refreshed and invigorated will reap rewards.

Alongside physical activity, you should have other interests. Do something you love that gives you an instant feeling of calm and relaxation. This may be a favourite hobby, a creative outlet like drawing, knitting or crafting. Alternatively, if you like cooking, then baking a cake or making supper is the perfect stress reliever. Or set up a jigsaw that you can dip into when you need a breather, as this type of puzzle uses both sides of your brain simultaneously and encourages a meditative state. We would recommend setting a timer for this or you risk being carried away with the determination of placing just one more piece!

QUIZ 7

SPELLING

Spell the following five words:

1. **ANECDYSIS (PRON: AN-EK-DYE-SIS):**

    the period between moults for animals who shed their
    body shells.

    EXAMPLE: There is usually no further development of
    the body during anecdysis.

2. **SCAPHOPOD (PRON: SKAF-A-POD):**

    a member of a class of marine molluscs.

    EXAMPLE: There are around 500 existing species of
    scaphopod.

3. **BECCAFICO (PRON: BEK-A-FEE-KOH):**

    a European songbird, eaten as a delicacy in Italy and
    some other countries.

    EXAMPLE: The beccafico is particularly fond of ripe figs.

4. **OMPHALOSKEPSIS (PRON: OM-FA-LOH-SKEP-SISS):**

self-absorbed contemplation.

EXAMPLE: He wants to stir the university out of its omphaloskepsis.

5. **PROPAEDEUTICAL (PRON: PROH-PI-DYOO-TI-KUL):**

preliminary or introductory.

EXAMPLE: You may prepare for the course by undertaking other kinds of propaedeutical activity.

COMPREHENSION

Pick the correct definition of the following words:

1. **SALTIMBOCCA (PRON: SAL-TIM-BOC-CA)**

   a) The saltimbocca plant grows a metre tall and is harvested in May.

   b) Maria declared that the best saltimbocca she had ever tasted was when she lived in Italy.

   c) The Smith family were the envy of the street with their new saltimbocca car.

2. **ROOIBOS (PRON: ROY-BOSS)**

   a) Emily's grandma likes all sorts of different tea, but her favourite is made from the rooibos plant.

   b) The rooibos is very similar to the kangaroo, only much smaller.

   c) Men who live in extremely cold countries wear a fur-lined hat called a rooibos.

3.   HUGUENOT (PRON: HYOOH-GAN-OH)

a) The Huguenot was the bestselling small car of 2012.

b) It was not uncommon for a Huguenot to flee to a Protestant country in fear of their life.

c) Apples and salmon are the main foods eaten on the Huguenot diet.

4.   CONCATENATE (PRON: KON-KAT-A-NAYT)

a) The vet performed a concatenate on the distressed horse and saved its life.

b) After his presentation, the main speaker was asked to concatenate his main points to the delegates.

c) The teacherless class made such a concatenate of noise that it was heard throughout the school.

5.   OVOVIVIPAROUS (PRON: OH-VOH-VYE-VA-PEHRAS)

a) Some fish and reptiles are ovoviviparous which means their eggs hatch within the body of the parent.

b) To become an ovoviviparous, you have to live at least until you are ninety.

c) Ovoviviparous is a tropical disease that is airborne and can be fatal.

MENTAL MATHS

MULTIPLICATION

1.   525.4 x 8 =

2.   753.6 x 9 =

3.   434.4 x 5 =

ADDITION

1.   75 + 20 + 68 + 66 + 42 + 22 =

2.   65 + 52 + 41 + 99 + 55 + 85 =

3.   79 + 79 + 82 + 94 + 66 + 61 =

SUBTRACTION

1.   755 - 85.4 =

2.   600 - 59.4 =

3.   512 - 91.7 =

DIVISION

1. $37.5 \div 3 =$
2. $65.7 \div 9 =$
3. $46.5 \div 3 =$

MIXED CALCULATIONS

1. $28 \times 6 - 14 \times 8 \div 7 =$
2. $17 \times 6 - 17 \times 2 \div 5 =$
3. $22 \times 5 - 25 \times 3 \div 5 =$

MENSA CHALLENGE

1. Cat is to kitten as cow is to

   a) Foal

   b) Calf

   c) Cub

2. How many more 4s are there than 3s?

1	5	7	2	9	6	4	0
8	4	9	7	3	1	2	4
7	3	4	1	3	5	9	1
7	6	55	4	1	22	6	4
3	1	0	2	77	4	5	8

3. What is the missing number?

   109, 67, 42, ?, 17, 8

4. There are 60 sweets in a bag. A quarter are cracked and a third are chipped. How many sweets are not damaged?

5. How many triangles can you see?

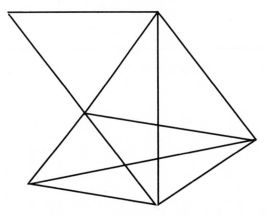

6. Add one letter to complete one word and start the other. OVA (....) OOP

7. If A = 1, B = 2, C = 3 and so on what is the total value of the word PIT?

8. What is the next number?

   93, 58, 35, 23, 12, ?

9. Lemon juice must be diluted 3 parts water to one of juice. In millilitres, how much juice is there in 284ml of diluted drink?

10. How many squares can you see?

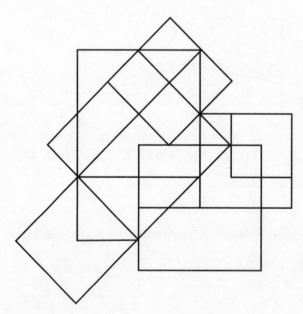

HISTORY

1. Dutty Boukman led a slave revolt on which island in the Caribbean?

2. Leaders of 12 European countries signed which treaty on 7 February 1992?

3. What became the 49th American state in 1959?

4. Which African country gained independence from South Africa in 1990?

5. Which country, a major Asian economy, entered a recession in June 1998?

6. In revolutionary France, who led the Committee of Public Safety until his downfall in July 1794?

7. The Bay of Pigs expedition was a failed invasion of which country?

8. Which philosopher was executed in 399 BC after upsetting politicians in Athens?

9. What was the name of the counting frame that Victorian children used as a calculator?

10. Which French king was executed on 21 January 1793?

GENERAL KNOWLEDGE

1. By what name is sodium chloride better known?

2. Cosmonaut, Valentina Tereshkova was the first woman in space in 1963, but what nationality was she?

3. Technically, there are only four ink colours used in colour printing, cyan, magenta, black and which other colour?

4. What is the second-largest ocean in the world?

5. *The Lion King* is a musical play based on the 1994 animated feature film by which American film producers?

6. Which country's capital is Vienna?

7. What does the 'A' stand for in the abbreviation DNA?

8. During the ongoing Battle of Britain, which prime minister declared before parliament: 'Never in the field of human conflict was so much owed by so many to so few'?

9. In athletics, how many hurdles are jumped over in the men's 110m hurdles race?

10. In which Spanish city would you find the famous Guggenheim Museum, which is said to resemble a ship?

11. Bharatanatyam (PRON: BURRA-TE-NAR-TEUM) is a classical dance mostly performed by women originating in which country?

12. In which country is the Giant Magellan telescope being built which will produce images ten times sharper than the Hubble Space Telescope?

13. Which African country's capital is Lusaka?

14. Which book by Antoine de Saint-Exupéry has sold more than 80 million copies?

15. Situated in Siberia, what is the name of the deepest freshwater lake in the world?

SCIENCE

1. What is the one-word term used to describe a mixture of fog and dust or soot in the air?

2. What type of electromagnetic waves are used to produce photographic pictures of inside the body?

3. Two electrically charged particles will repel each other if their charges are what?

4. A biennial plant lives for how many years?

5. Amphibians, birds and fish are all examples of what taxonomic rank?

6. Methanoic and ethanoic acid are examples of what general type of acid?

7. Coal, oil and gas are all types of what fuel?

8. What is the chemical formula for the soft silvery-white reactive metal, potassium?

9. What name is given to the trapping of solar energy by atmospheric carbon dioxide?

10. Which body in our solar system is covered by jets of gas called spicules?

ADVANCED LANGUAGE

Solve the following five anagrams:

1. **g e y n e h i**

   The science concerned with the maintenance of health.

2. **s o u r t i d o c u s e**

   Showing bad manners; impolite; rude.

3. **d e p a r l c u p i n r e**

   At right angles to a horizontal plane.

4. **m a t i b e l c o i n p**

   Incapable of living or existing together in peace or harmony; conflicting or antagonistic.

5. **p e d i t e x n e**

   Inclined towards methods or means that are advantageous, rather than fair or just.

SUDDEN DEATH

Calculate: 28 x 7 - 24 x 7 ÷ 2 =

ANSWERS

COMPREHENSION

1. b) Maria declared that the best saltimbocca she had
    ever tasted was when she lived in Italy.
    DEF: a dish consisting of rolled pieces of veal or poultry
    cooked with herbs, bacon and other flavourings.

2. a) Emily's grandma likes all sorts of different tea, but her
    favourite is made from the rooibos plant.
    DEF: an evergreen South African shrub of the pea
    family.

3. b) It was not uncommon for a Huguenot to flee to a
    Protestant country in fear of their life.
    DEF: a French Protestant of the 16th and 17th
    centuries.

4. b) After his presentation, the main speaker was asked to
    concatenate his main points to the delegates.

DEF: link (things) together in a chain or series.

5. a) Some fish and reptiles are ovoviviparous which means their eggs hatch within the body of the parent.
DEF: (of an animal) producing young by means of eggs which are hatched with the body of the parent, as in some snakes.

MENTAL MATHS
Multiplication
1. 4203.2
2. 6782.4
3. 2172

Addition
1. 293
2. 397
3. 461

Subtraction
1. 669.6

2.   540.6

3.   420.3

Division

1.   12.5

2.   7.3

3.   15.5

Mixed Calculations

1.   176

2.   34

3.   51

MENSA CHALLENGE

1.   Calf

2.   3

3.   25

4.   25

5.   25

6.   L OVA (L) OOP

7.   45

8.   11

9. 71ml
10. 17
11. 4
12. 52
13. 480 (300 for £5, therefore £1 buys 60 minutes, 60 x 8 = 480/8 hours, but we ask for minutes, so no one should give the answer 8)
14. 18

HISTORY

1. Hispaniola (ACCEPT: Saint Domingue/Haiti)
2. Maastricht Treaty (ACCEPT: Maastricht Final Act)
3. Alaska
4. Namibia
5. Japan
6. Maximilien Robespierre
7. Cuba
8. Socrates
9. Abacus
10. Louis XVI

GENERAL KNOWLEDGE

1. Salt

2. Russian

3. Yellow

4. Atlantic

5. Walt Disney (ACCEPT: Disney)

6. Austria

7. Acid (Deoxyribose Nucleic Acid)

8. Winston Churchill

9. Ten

10. Bilbao

11. India

12. Chile

13. Zambia

14. *Le Petit Prince*(ACCEPT: *The Little Prince*)

15. Lake Baikal

SCIENCE

1. Smog

2. X-rays

3. The same (ACCEPT: identical)
4. Two
5. Classes
6. Carboxylic
7. Fossil fuels
8. K
9. Greenhouse effect (NB: carbon dioxide is not the only gas involved but this does not affect the answer.)
10. The Sun

ADVANCED LANGUAGE

1. hygiene
2. discourteous
3. perpendicular
4. incompatible
5. expedient

SUDDEN DEATH

602

☉ Did You Know? ☉

How to Identify Your Style of Working

Understanding how we learn best is key to achieving the results we want. When we are stressed, under pressure and feeling overwhelmed with the tasks ahead, we find it hard to be effective. Making a few adjustments to our approach, environment and attitude can positively affect our learning outcomes. The secret is to identify exactly what style of working suits us and stick to it.

There are those of us who thrive in a structured classroom situation, amongst our peers, whilst others learn better through more visual means, at different times of the day or away from distraction. Knowing which category you fall into is a good place to start. If you consider the key elements to how you work, you can then create the right environment to succeed. Do you learn best visually, verbally, methodically, socially or independently? How easily distracted are you? What timetable works best? Asking yourself these questions will start to build a picture of your ideal working approach.

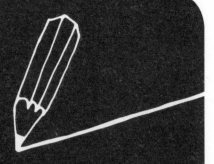

The same philosophy can be applied to finding the learning techniques that work best for you. There is a mnemonic device out there for everyone, whether it involves repetition, list making, the **Method of Loci** (see page 250), acronyms or acrostics. You should consider your working environment: do you focus better facing a wall to avoid distractions or need a window with a view? It is unlikely any of us can work well in front of the TV, but silence can be just as diverting, so an appropriate background playlist sometimes helps. Being comfortable generally – the right chair, room temperature, hydration, accessible reference books – may take a few moments to organise, but can make a big difference to long-term concentration. Some of us operate better at the beginning of the day, whereas others come to life much later.

Spending time thinking about the sort of student you are and how to realise your full potential will save you time and anxiety in the long run.

SPELLING

Spell the following five words:

1. **TROUSSEAU (PRON: TRUE-SOH):**
    the clothes, linen and other belongings collected by a bride for her marriage.
    EXAMPLE: Felicity kept her trousseau in an antique armoire.

2. **CHLAMYDOMONAS (PRON: KLA-MID-A-MOH-NUS):**
    a green, fresh water algae that is made up of a single cell.
    EXAMPLE: Chlamydomonas is commonly seen in lakes in Antarctica.

3. **STYGIAN (PRON: STIDJ-JEE-UHN):**
    very dark.
    EXAMPLE: A black robe, a papier-mâché sickle and some greyish make-up completed Sean's Stygian Halloween costume.

4.   **GYRODYNE (PRON: JYE-ROH-DINE):**
     an aircraft with a rotor that is powered during take-off
     and manoeuvring, but not when cruising.
     EXAMPLE: The gyrodyne attempts to provide
     helicopter-like low-speed performance.

5.   **AUTOCHTHON (PRON: AW-TOK-THUN):**
     one of the earliest known inhabitants of any country.
     EXAMPLE: He was not an autochthon of the North
     American colonies.

COMPREHENSION

Pick the correct definition of the following words:

1. **VIGNETTE (PRON: VIN-YET)**
   a) As an aside, the teacher gave a vignette of France, to illustrate his point.
   b) It is essential to shake vignette before pouring it over salad leaves.
   c) Hiding in the vignette, Mary could hear everyone searching for her.

2. **AXIOMATIC (PRON: AKSI-O-MATIK)**
   a) An axiomatic is essential to the study of geometry.
   b) The axiomatic setting is the fastest cycle on the washing machine.
   c) Barbara hated it when her mum used really obvious and axiomatic phrases.

3. **CAPRICIOUS (PRON: KA-PRISH-US)**
   a) Tegan's mum thinks her capricious behaviour is due to eating too many sweets.

b) My favourite drink is a capricious coffee with lashings of cream and chocolate on it.

c) Eve was very proud of her new capricious curtains which made the room look luxurious.

4.   MALADROIT (PRON: MAL-A-DROYT)

a) The physio massaged the footballer's back to relieve his maladroit.

b) Maladroit ducks are the most common variety and often seen at park lakes.

c) When the school trip was cancelled, it made the teacher unhappy about the maladroit way the matter had been handled.

5.   OTORHINOLARYNGOLOGY (PRON: OH-TOH-RYE-NOH-LAR-ING-GOL-EJI)

a) Visiting the otorhinolaryngology enclosure in the zoo allows spectators to watch lions closely.

b) It takes many years of study to become a specialist in otorhinolaryngology.

c) Otorhinolaryngology is a very grand name for sea sickness.

MENTAL MATHS

MULTIPLICATION

1.   228.2 x 9 =
2.   797.8 x 5 =
3.   653.1 x 7 =

ADDITION

1.   122 + 931+ 909 +658 =
2.   127 +123 + 641 + 645 =
3.   800 + 552 + 598 + 716 =

SUBTRACTION

1.   673 - 76.1 =
2.   650 - 95.2 =
3.   876 - 62.2 =

PERCENTAGES

1. 35% of 500 =
2. 60% of 175 =
3. 40% of375 =

MIXED CALCULATIONS

1. 14 x 4 - 27 x 8 ÷ 2 =
2. 26 x 7 - 10 x 2 ÷ 8 =
3. 10 x 2 - 10 x 4 ÷ 5 =

MENSA CHALLENGE

1. Eagle is to bird as mouse is to:

    a) reptile

    b) rodent

    c) insect

2. How many more 2s are there than 6s?

77	2	5	2	1	6	5	8
4	1	2	3	0	2	1	6
3	5	6	4	2	1	2	7
5	2	0	1	5	8	6	9
2	8	9	2	6	0	3	2

3. What is the next number? 52, 56, 62, 70, 80, ?

4. A paperboy earns £56 in 8 weeks. In pounds, how much does he earn in 12 weeks?

5. How many triangles can you see?

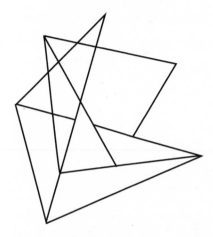

6. Add one letter to complete one word and start the other:
    OVE (...) AVY

7. If A = 1, B = 2, C = 3 and so on, what is the total value
    of the word WHO?

8. What is the missing number? 4, 5, 9, ?, 23, 37

9. Coaches seat 34 children. 83 children go on a school trip. How many children are on the coach that is not full?

10. How many squares can you see?

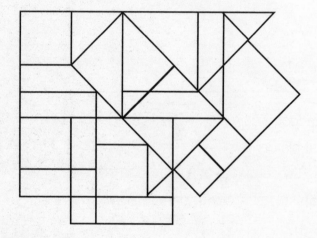

HISTORY

1. Which country was an observer state for many years before joining the United Nations on 10 September 2002?

2. What was the first novel by Charles Dickens?

3. Thucydides' account of which war is considered to be one of the first history books?

4. In Beijing, protests in which square ended in bloodshed on 4 June 1989?

5. Aristotle was a pupil of which other philosopher?

6. In which American city did major anti-globalisation protests erupt when a meeting of the World Trade Organization was held there in 1999?

7.   In 1510, Goa became the principal Portuguese base in which country?

8.   To which Soviet leader did John F. Kennedy deliver an ultimatum in October 1962?

9.   In which play by Aristophanes do Aeschylus and Euripides have a dispute over who is the best poet?

10. Which French author wrote *Le Deuxième Sexe*?

GENERAL KNOWLEDGE

1. How long, in days, is the Christian festival Lent?

2. Which planet is fifth from the Sun and the largest planet in our solar system?

3. What is the name of Japan's capital city?

4. Which mineral composed of pure carbon is the hardest known naturally occurring substance?

5. Which is the longest river in Europe?

6. The tallest man-made structure on land in the world is the Burj Khalifa. In which city would you find this building?

7. The Gunpowder Plot was a conspiracy by a small group of Catholic extremists to blow up which English king and his parliament on 5 November 1605?

8. What is the name of the US space shuttle that exploded in 1986, shortly after its launch?

9. In which country was printing by blocks invented in the seventh century?

10. What is the chemical formula for the element iron?

11. What is the name of the capital city of Oman?

12. What is the school of design, architecture and applied arts that existed in Germany from 1919 to 1933?

13. In which country is the Nurek Dam, one of the world's tallest dams?

14. Which event in the USA, also known as Black Thursday, occurred on 24 October 1929 and contributed to the Great Depression?

15. Which Impressionist artist painted *Four Ballerinas on the Stage*?

SCIENCE

1. Which is the largest planet of the solar system, consisting of gas and liquid and with no solid surface?

2. What name is given to a period of dormancy for animals during the winter?

3. The reaction which breaks large alkanes into smaller alkanes and alkenes is called what?

4. Which unit, with the abbreviation dB, is used to measure the intensity of sound?

5. Mars has two small moons. Phobos is one, what is the name of the other?

6. 'The Archer' is the English name for which constellation?

7. Which metal has the chemical symbol Hg?

8. What is the main ingredient of natural gas?

9. Which property of a substance is obtained by dividing its mass by its volume?

10. The large gap between Saturn's A Ring and B Ring is known by what name?

ADVANCED LANGUAGE

Solve the following five anagrams:

1. **t u f h a r g**

   Showing or producing tension or anxiety.

2. **s a p o v i d l a r p**

   Unfavourable opinion; condemnation.

3. **t i m e l a m i r a**

   Of no real importance; inconsequential.

4. **n i a i t i n e d f i t o c**

   The process of recognizing specific objects as the result of remembering.

5. **a r e r e d y i t h**

   Of, relating to, or denoting factors that can be transmitted genetically from one generation to another.

SUDDEN DEATH

Calculate: 44523 + 6948 =

ANSWERS

COMPREHENSION

1.   a) As an aside the teacher gave a vignette of France, to illustrate his point.
     DEF: a brief evocative description, account or episode.

2.   c) Barbara hated it when her mum used really obvious and axiomatic phrases.
     DEF: self-evident or unquestionable.

3.   a) Tegan's mum thinks her capricious behaviour is due to eating too many sweets.
     DEF: given to sudden and unaccountable changes of mood or behavior.

4.   c) When the school trip was cancelled, it made the teacher unhappy about the maladroit way the matter had been handled.
     DEF: inefficient or inept; clumsy.

5. b) It takes many years of study to become a specialist in otorhinolaryngology.

    DEF: the study of diseases of the ear, nose and throat.

MENTAL MATHS
Multiplication
1. 2053.8
2. 3989
3. 4571.7

Addition
1. 2620
2. 1536
3. 2666

Subtraction
1. 596.9
2. 554.8
3. 813.8

Percentages
1. 175
2. 105

3.   150

Mixed Calculations

1.   116
2.   43
3.   8

MENSA CHALLENGE

1.   Rodent
2.   5
3.   92
4.   £84 (56 ÷ 8 = 7, 7 x 12 = 84)
5.   18
6.   OVE (N) AVY

   NB: OVED/DAVY; OVES/SAVY. At least one in each pair is found in Oxford Online, but not in the *Oxford English Dictionary*, so would therefore not be allowed.
7.   46
8.   14
9.   15
10.   17

HISTORY

1.   Switzerland

2.   *The Pickwick Papers*

3.   Peloponnesian War

4.   Tiananmen Square

5.   Plato

6.   Seattle

7.   India

8.   Nikita Khrushchev

9.   *The Frogs*

10. Simone de Beauvoir

GENERAL KNOWLEDGE

1.   40

2.   Jupiter

3.   Tokyo

4.   Diamond

5.   Volga

6.   Dubai, United Arab Emirates (DO NOT ACCEPT: UAE)

7.   King James I – King James I of England (VI of Scotland)

8.   *Challenger*

9.   China

10. Fe

11. Muscat

12. Bauhaus

13. Tajikistan

14. The Wall Street Crash

15. Edgar Degas (ACCEPT: Degas)

SCIENCE

1.   Jupiter

2.   Hibernation

3.   Cracking

4.   Decibel

5.   Deimos

6.   Sagittarius

7.   Mercury

8.   Methane

9.   Density

10. Cassini Division

ADVANCED LANGUAGE

1. fraught
2. disapproval
3. immaterial
4. identification
5. hereditary

SUDDEN DEATH

51471

♀ Did You Know? ♀

The Power of Mnemonics

You may not be familiar with the word mnemonic, but it's likely to have helped you when trying to learn and retain knowledge. It is the name given to the techniques that encourage us to remember facts, a way of encoding our brain to understand, store and then retrieve information. The strategies include converting lists to acronyms and acrostics, turning facts into musical poems, picturing visual triggers and simple data ordering. Thought to have originated from Ancient Greece, the word 'mnemonics' comes from the Greek word for 'memory or mindful' and is pronounced nemonics (the first 'm' is silent). It relies on the power of patterns which make it easier for your incredible memory to work and produce the right answers when you need them.

There are several effective mnemonic devices that you can turn to, depending on the subject you are revising and how your brain best processes information. One of the most popular strategies is **first-letter** mnemonics, where you create a list of single-word facts and take the capital letter from each to form an **acronym** that can then be constructed into an easy to recall sentence. This works brilliantly when studying ordered facts like the planets, musical notes and colours of the rainbow. For example, rainbows are made up of seven colours – **r**ed, **o**range, **y**ellow, **g**reen, **b**lue, **i**ndigo and **v**iolet. The acronym for this is ROYGBIV, which is a tricky mouthful of letters to remember – that is, until we give them an **acrostic** sentence to sit in like this traditional one: **R**ichard **of** **Y**ork **g**ave **b**attle **in** **v**ain.

Not all facts work with this method; many lend themselves better to being turned into a **song** or **rhyme**, another great mnemonic tactic. Why try and memorise the list of the kings and queens of England when you can sing it instead (see page 282 to find out more)? Alternatively, try visualisation, a technique beneficial for those who learn best through imagery known as the **Method of Loci** (more on this on page 250). Or break information into bite-size **chunks** and sort into clear sections, so the mass of work to remember is not overwhelming. It gives your brain a much better chance of retaining and retrieving it for you.

💡 Did You Know? 💡

The Method of Loci

The **Method of Loci** is thought to be the oldest memory technique in the world, traced back to Ancient Greece and Rome. This mnemonic system relies on imagery and visualisation to encourage the brain to remember facts by picturing them in a familiar place and associating them with key objects. Hence the term 'loci', the Latin word for place or location. Legend has it that it was discovered by a Greek poet who was the only survivor of a building collapse. To enable him to recall who else had been in the room, he pictured all the guests at the dining table. Through visualising where people sat and who they spoke to, he could piece together a list of all those who had perished.

The Romans also spotted the power of using familiar environments as an effective way to remember vital information. They practised a similar method which relied on mentally walking through each room in their house and storing information that could then be retrieved using triggers.

It may sound complicated, but think of this technique in the context of

a 'memory palace' and try using you own house as a template. Or go on a 'memory journey', recalling a route you know very well and assigning information to points of interest along the way. It is thought that these techniques are successful because of the way the brain orders facts and associates with physical place. Recently, the concept of the mind palace was highlighted by Benedict Cumberbatch's TV portrayal of Sherlock Holmes, albeit a fictitious and exceptional version of it.

Loci is invaluable to Memory Champions who compete, but it doesn't work for everyone or in all situations. We need the right mnemonic tool for the right studying job, and whilst this technique has tried-and-tested results, it isn't always the one to use. Be warned that it is time consuming, needs good visual ability and works best on a more complex level of association. It is not enough to just imagine a room in your house and recall the facts you learnt without having attached them to an object, person or event. The more bizarre the better.

⚐ Did You Know? ⚐

Rhymes and How They Can Help

'Incey Wincey Spider', 'Jack and Jill', 'Twinkle Twinkle Little Star' and 'Little Miss Muffet' are just a few of the traditional, beloved rhymes that we are taught as children and, in turn, teach to the generations that follow. These rhymes are often our first experience of storytelling and music, and are much more important than we may realise. They are responsible for introducing us to language, communication and music before we can talk. Rhyme encourages us to use words and to recognise syllables, sounds and repetition which then creates a basis for our future education. This enables us to understand our phonics, helps with spelling and supports us in learning to read. The same devices can be used to just as good effect as we get older and are a valuable mnemonic tool. Let's look at times tables. This feels like an impossible task and the bigger multiplications elude us initially, so using a rhyming tactic is very effective. It is pretty hard to forget this sum 8 x 8 = 64 if we turn it into: 'He ate and ate and was sick on the floor, 8 x 8 = 64'. We are taking the same principles from our nursery-rhyme years here and transferring them into our further education. Through this approach we can teach ourselves historical facts too. How do we remember what befell each of King Henry VIII's six wives? We use the famous little ditty – divorced, beheaded, died, divorced, beheaded, survived – and worry no more. Rhyming can also be vital in absorbing a new language, as creating a melody and rhythm around words helps the brain to store information easily. There are many rhymes online to help us learn, but often the best are those we make up ourselves.

SPELLING

Spell the following five words:

1. **ROTOGRAVURE (PRON: ROTO-GRAV-VURE):**
    a printing system using a rotary press with intaglio
    cylinders, typically running at high speed and used for
    long print runs of magazines and stamps.
    EXAMPLE: The printers would love to find a sheet
    suitable for rotogravure that is not exorbitantly priced.

2. **OSSICLE (PRON: OSS-SICK-AL):**
    a very small bone, especially one of those in the middle
    ear.
    EXAMPLE: The doctor told Marcus that an ossicle in
    his left ear had been damaged by the blow in his boxing
    match.

3. **OREAD (PRON: ORR-REE-AD):**

   a nymph believed to inhabit mountains.

   EXAMPLE: The painting featured an oread assisting Artemis in the hunt.

4. **ANTEBELLUM (PRON: AN-TI-BEL-UM):**

   referring to the period before a war, especially the American Civil War.

   EXAMPLE: More than two-fifths of antebellum American women worked outside their homes.

5. **KERSEYMERE (PRON: KER-ZI-MEER):**

   a fine woollen cloth.

   EXAMPLE: The narrow coat of grey kerseymere had long, straight skirts and a high collar.

COMPREHENSION

Pick the correct definition of the following words:

1. UMBRAGE (PRON: UM-BRIDGE)

a) Jennifer had always wanted to umbrage her hair, but her mum wouldn't let her.

b) An umbrage is a small passageway between two caves.

c) Max took umbrage at everyone's dislike of his new leather jacket.

2. WRANGLE (PRON: RAN-GUL)

a) A wrangle is a necklace worn tight around the neck.

b) The lawyers continue to wrangle over the fine print of Lisa's contract.

c) If you wrangle a pair of jeans they get a really cool, washed-out look.

3. **APPROBATION (PRON: APP-RO-BAY-SHUN)**

   a) After many months, the council has finally indicated its approbation of the plans.

   b) The approbation society are always on the lookout for new species of butterflies.

   c) An approbation officer visits the prisoners regularly.

4. **ABERRATION (PRON: ABB-UH-RAY-SHUN)**

   a) The doctor said that the aberration on Jake's head would need five stitches.

   b) The outbreak of violence in this usually quiet location was a temporary aberration.

   c) Dad asked for the aberration knife, so that he could carve the roast beef.

5. **PEDICULICIDE (PRON: PUH-DIK-YUH-LUH-SAHYD)**

   a) A pediculicide is the name for a bicycle with three seats.

   b) If you wear a pediculicide it will count how many steps you take in a day.

   c) A pediculicide is an effective agent for treating head lice.

MENTAL MATHS

MULTIPLICATION

1. 473.3 x 8 =
2. 761.7 x 8=
3. 217.6 x 8=

ADDITION

1. 23 + 53 + 69 + 20 + 70 + 66 =
2. 14 + 55 + 33 + 92 + 46 + 65 =
3. 67 + 67 + 50 + 70 + 96 + 66 =

SUBTRACTION

1. 4214 - 368 =
2. 4213 - 557 =
3. 4115 - 359 =

PERCENTAGES

1. 35% of 400 =

2. 70% of 200 =

3. 60% of 325 =

MIXED CALCULATIONS

1. 27 x 6 - 25 x 4 ÷ 2 =

2. 23 x 7 - 19 x 7 ÷ 2 =

3. 24 x 6 - 11 x 9 ÷ 3 =

MENSA CHALLENGE

1.   Add one letter to complete one word and start the other:
     HOL (...) ARD

2.   How many more 4s are there than 8s?

4	2	1	3	4	4	8	7
33	4	8	11	2	3	1	8
9	7	1	33	6	8	4	5
4	8	0	4	1	2	3	4
6	4	4	2	8	4	5	7

4.   What is the next number? 32, 20, 12, 8, 4, ?

5.   A train covers 475km in two and a half hours. Travelling
     at a constant speed, what distance does the train travel
     in an hour?

6.   How many squares can you see?

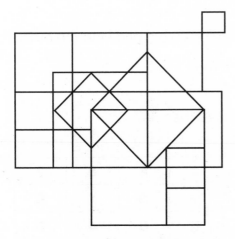

7.   Below is to under as above is to:

   a) beneath

   b) even

   c) over

8.   If A = 1, B = 2, C = 3 and so on, what is the total value
     of the word WON?

9. What is the missing number? 60, 62, 66, ?, 80, 90

10. Rani pays £63 for 9 cinema tickets. In pounds, how much will it cost for 12 tickets?

11. How many triangles can you see?

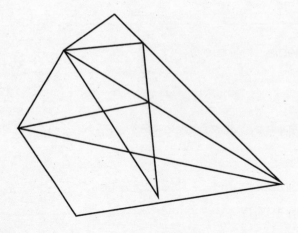

HISTORY

1. Which American city suffered a huge earthquake on 19 October 1989?

2. In Greek tragedy, Oedipus is so named because of damage to what part of his body?

3. Which British media magnate died on 5 November 1991?

4. In a play by Euripides, Hippolytus is the son of which hero?

5. Who was the spiritual leader of Tibet, who fled his country in March 1959?

6. Which Act of 1872 meant that people could cast their vote in secret?

7. Who designed the huge steam-powered ships, *Great Western* and *Great Eastern*?

8. The spread of which religion in East Africa was reinforced by the establishment of the Funj Sultanate of Sennar?

9. Which company's monopoly on trade to China was abolished in 1834?

10. Which word first appeared on the Waldseemüller world map in 1507?

GENERAL KNOWLEDGE

1. In music, what does the abbreviation R&B stand for?

2. China's capital is known by two names, Peking is one, what is the other?

3. How many Harry Potter books are in the series by J K Rowling?

4. What is the nickname of the aircraft used by NASA for weightless training for astronauts?

5. Which Jewish festival celebrates the release of the Israelites from Egyptian slavery?

6. Which is the only asteroid big enough to be classed as a dwarf planet?

7.   Named after the German physicist, which unit of frequency for measuring sound waves has the abbreviation Hz?

8.   Situated in Venezuela and reaching a height of approximately 979m, what is the highest waterfall in the world?

9.   Cholecalciferol is a natural form of which vitamin?

10. In which year did Princess Victoria become Queen at the age of 18?

11. The Battle of Trafalgar was fought on the 21st October 1805. Cape Trafalagar is off the coast of which European country?

12. In which US state would you find one of the youngest and best preserved meteor craters on Earth?

13. The capital city is Bogotá, what is the name of the country?

14. What is the total number of astronauts to have walked on the Moon?

15. Which English doctor discovered how to make magnets, and coined the term magnetic pole?

SCIENCE

1. What sort of device was used to slow the Huygens probe as it descended towards Titan in 2004?

2. Phytohormones are a type of hormone produced by what?

3. The Venera probes that went to Venus were launched from Earth by which country?

4. Which quantity do you get by dividing the distance travelled by an object, by the time taken?

5. Jupiter's moon Europa has a crust made mainly of what?

6. As opposed to dark matter, what term do astronomers use for everything we can see or touch?

7. In a microwave oven, what name is given to the part that produces the microwaves?

8. The Southern Pinwheel is a spiral galaxy in which constellation?

9. An ammonia molecule has one nitrogen atom and how many hydrogen atoms?

10. What was the name of the rocket used for the Apollo Moon missions?

ADVANCED LANGUAGE

Solve the following five anagrams:

1. **r e d c i l e t**

   Deserted or abandoned, as by an owner, occupant, etc.

2. **i o n n a m e d r o t**

   The divisor of a fraction, as 8 in 7/8.

3. **m o t o h e y p a h**

   A system of medical treatment based on the theory
   that certain diseases can be cured by giving very small
   doses of drugs which in a healthy person would produce
   symptoms like those of the disease.

4. **l o n g a g e y e**

   The direct descent of an individual from an ancestor.

5. **r u m r u l c u c i**

   A course of study in one subject at a school or college.

SUDDEN DEATH

Calculate: 12 x 8 - 18 x 3 ÷ 9 =

ANSWERS

COMPREHENSION

1. c) Max took umbrage at everyone's dislike of his new leather jacket.

    DEF: offence or annoyance; archaic, shade or shadow, especially as cast by trees.

2. b) The lawyers continue to wrangle over the fine print of Lisa's contract.

    DEF: noun – a dispute or argument, typically one that is long and complicated; verb – have a long, complicated dispute or argument.

3. a) After many months, the council has finally indicated its approbation of the plans.

    DEF: formal, approval or praise.

4. b) The outbreak of violence in this usually quiet location was a temporary aberration.

DEF: a departure from what is normal, usual or expected, typically an unwelcome one.

5.   c) A pediculicide is an effective agent for treating head lice.
DEF: a chemical used to kill lice.

MENTAL MATHS
Multiplication
1.   3786.4
2.   6093.6
3.   1740.8

Addition
1.   301
2.   305
3.   416

Subtraction
1.   3846
2.   3656
3.   3756

Percentages

1. 14
2. 140
3. 195

Mixed Calculations

1. 274
2. 497
3. 399

MENSA CHALLENGE

1. HOL (Y) ARD or HOL (S) ARD
2. 5
3. 4
4. 190km (475 ÷ 2.5 = 190)
5. 19
6. Over
7. 52 (23 + 15 + 14 = 52)
8. 72
9. £84 (63 ÷ 9 = 7 x 12 = £84)
10. 26

HISTORY

1. San Francisco (ACCEPT: San Francisco-Oakland)
2. Feet (ACCEPT: foot)
3. Robert Maxwell
4. Theseus
5. The Dalai Lama
6. Ballot Act
7. Isambard Kingdom Brunel
8. Islam
9. British East India Company
10. America

GENERAL KNOWLEDGE

1. Rhythm and Blues
2. Beijing
3. 7
4. Vomit comet
5. Passover (ACCEPT: Pesach (in Hebrew))
6. Ceres
7. Hertz

8. Angel Falls (ACCEPT: Salto Angel/Parakupa Vena/ Kerepakupai Merú)

9. Vitamin D

10. 1837

11. Spain

12. Arizona

13. Colombia

14. 12

15. William Gilbert

SCIENCE

1. Parachute

2. Plants

3. Russia (ACCEPT: Soviet Union)

4. Average speed (DO NOT ACCEPT : Velocity)

5. Ice

6. Ordinary matter (ACCEPT: ordinary atomic matter/ baryonic matter)

7. Magnetron

8. Hydra

9. Three
10. Saturn V (Five)

ADVANCED LANGUAGE

1. derelict
2. denominator
3. homeopathy
4. genealogy
5. curriculum

SUDDEN DEATH

26

♀ Did You Know? ♀

How to Remember the Order of the Planets

It is one thing to remember names but quite another to get them in the right sequence. There are only eight planets to remember, so **visualising** them is a good tactic, in order from the one nearest to the Sun and working back through the solar system. We have the smallest planet Mercury, followed by Venus which has the longest rotation around the Sun and then our home Earth. The red-hued Mars is next, then the largest planet Jupiter, with a faint ring around its middle. Gassy Saturn is the second-largest planet, Uranus, known for its ice and rock is seventh in the solar system and chilly Neptune is the eighth and farthest from the Sun. If you find it harder to picture these facts, then try other **mnemonic** methods we discuss in this book instead – maybe by **verbally** recanting them or repeatedly **writing** them down. One way is to break the list down into the **acronym** MVEMJSUN. Another suggestion is to use the acronym and create a sentence out of it. To give you an idea, a popular **acrostic** of MVEMJSUN is: My Very Educated Mother Just Served Us

Noodles. But you can easily create your own version. This is a great way to learn all sorts of lists. You can also turn the planet order into a **song** or **poem** and there are various examples of this online. Numbering each planet or visualising them with their own unique qualities may work better for you. The trick is to find the technique your memory best responds to and stick with that through all the educational systems you may orbit.

♀ Did You Know? ♀

Tricks to Remember the Kings and Queens of England

Who can forget Queen Victoria, Queen Elizabeth I and King Henry VIII – all big personalities with amazing lives to learn about, but do you know who ruled before each of them came to the throne? Learning the full list of rulers by name and in order of succession, especially when some of those names are repeated several times, is no mean feat. This is exactly the type of monumental task that benefits from using a selection of **mnemonic** devices (more on page 248). The most popular and traditional of these is **rhyme** (find out why rhyme works on page 252). There are many variations of an age-old verse used by school children back in the days when learning was by repetition. One version begins with Egbert and the Saxons, but more commonly with the Normans and William the Conqueror. It names each of the rulers in order with catchy abbreviations, and can be sung to a tune:

Willie, Willie, Harry, Stee,

Harry, Dick, John, Harry Three,

One-To-Three Neds, Richard Two,

Harrys Four-Five-Six...then who?

Edwards Four-Five, Dick the Bad,

Harrys (twain), Ned Six (the lad),

Mary, Bessie, James you ken,

Then Charlie, Charlie, James again...

Will & Mary, Anne of gloria,

Georges (4!), Will Four, Victoria,

Edward Seven next, and then

Came George the Fifth in 1910...

Ned the Eighth soon abdicated,

So George Six was coronated,

Then Number Two Elizabeth...

And that's all, folks (until her death...)!

One of the key successes to remembering names is to associate them with something that will remain etched in our minds; in this instance, learning each ruler alongside a **memorable fact**: Henry VIII had six wives, Richard II became king at the age of ten and so on. This helps us to recall them, but is not as useful when keeping everyone in order. The successful BBC children's show *Horrible Histories* wrote and performed their own version called 'The 'Rulers' Song', with additional facts as reminders of what some were infamous for or how they met a sticky end.

Those of us who respond better through **imagery** could draw a family tree or a timeline and memorise that way. This is a more time-consuming process, but it does result in an illustrative aid we can continue to refer back to.

Another trick is to use the **chunking** strategy which can work at this level of recall. Breaking the list into the Royal Houses – Norman, Plantagenet, Lancaster, York, Tudor, Stuart, Hanover, Saxe-Coburg-Gotha and Windsor – and remembering the **acronym** NPLYTSHSW (with a silly sentence that uses the first letter of each) is a good start. Then we can learn the rulers house by house in date order. The **Method of Loci** (see page 250), using imagery to store information, is an ancient-civilisation technique that could also help. Imagine your house and designate each Royal House a room within it, so Normans in the kitchen, Lancasters in the bathroom, etc. Then position each of the rulers in their rightful room and further cement this memory by assigning them an object or adding detail. Just think of poor old Charles I who was beheaded, standing by your fireplace holding his head under his arm.

SPELLING

Spell the following five words:

1. **PURSLANE (PRON: PURS-LAN):**

    any of a number of small, typically fleshy-leaved plants which grow in damp or marshy habitats.

    EXAMPLE: Roberta ordered a delicious salad of purslane and other greens at the vegetarian café.

2. **ASPHALT (PRON: ASS-FALT):**

    a mixture of dark, bituminous pitch with sand or gravel, used for surfacing roads, flooring, roofing, etc; the pitch used in asphalt, sometimes found in natural deposits but usually made by the distillation of crude oil.

    EXAMPLE: Smooth asphalt makes the coastal road a favourite for both drivers and cyclists.

3. **DIMINUENDO (PRON: DI-MIN-U-EN-DOH):**

    a decrease in loudness in a piece of music.

    EXAMPLE: During the diminuendo, the flutes in the orchestra became more prominent.

4. **KURTOSIS (PRON: KA-TOE-SISS):**

    a statistical measure used to describe the distribution of data.

    EXAMPLE: Figure 8 shows three symmetrical curves with different degrees of kurtosis.

5. **AMANUENSIS (PRON: A-MAN-YOO-EN-SIS):**

    a person who is employed to write down words that are dictated to them or to copy manuscripts.

    EXAMPLE: Paul checked his amanuensis's final draft, since he was ultimately responsible for the letter.

COMPREHENSION

Pick the correct definition of the following words:

1. **HIDALGO (PRON: HE-DALL-GO)**

   a) The hidalgo was hidden behind a rock and kept the beaver family dry.

   b) To hidalgo proficiently, you need to practise at least three hours a day.

   c) The Spanish dance performed by the hidalgo drew gasps from the tourists.

2. **ECLOGUE (PRON: ECK-LOG)**

   a) Never eclogue custard as it will result in curdling.

   b) Marnie's eclogue about her holiday in the countryside, was by far her best.

   c) The eclogue always meet at the front of the church before the procession.

3.   FUGACITY (PRON: FEW-GAS-I-TEE)

a) Ellen was glad she had fugacity to keep her wig secure.

b) When you smell fugacity in the air, you know someone is having an authentic curry.

c) The fugacity of the newspaper headline means that by tomorrow it will be old news.

4.   CORRIGENDUM (PRON: CORRA-JEN-DUM)

a) The proofreader thought she might scream if she had to put in another corrigendum in her book.

b) Michael's garden won first prize for his beautiful corrigendum blooms.

c) The corrigendum pass is frequented by climbers and hill walkers.

5.   PLEONASM (PRON: PLEE-UH-NAZM)

a) The pleonasm surrounding the Moon is visible on a clear night.

b) The use of a pleonasm in your essay will bring your mark down.

c) Adding a dash of pleonasm to your soup will spice it up.

MENTAL MATHS

MULTIPLICATION

1.   168.5 x 9 =
2.   168.1 x 5 =
3.   870.8 x 7 =

ADDITION

1.   71 + 88 + 24 + 38 + 29 + 38 =
2.   79 + 73 + 95 + 19 + 59 + 33 =
3.   15 + 61 + 49 + 77 + 86 + 55 =

SUBTRACTION

1.   892 - 86.5 =
2.   3633 - 957 =
3.   4325 - 658 =

PERCENTAGES

1. 30% of 350 =

2. 30% of 650 =

3. 60% of 275 =

MIXED CALCULATIONS

1. 30 x 5 - 18 x 7 ÷ 4 =

2. 28 x 7 - 24 x 7 ÷ 2 =

3. 12 x 8 - 18 x 3 ÷ 9 =

MENSA CHALLENGE

1. Compass is to direction as watch is to:
    a) time
    b) hours
    c) clock

2. If A = 1, B = 2, C = 3 and so on, what is the total value of the word KIT?

3. What is the missing number? 98, 90, 82, ?, 66, 58

4. Oil costs 75p a litre. In pounds and pence, how much will it cost to fill a 50-litre tank?

5. How many triangles can you see?

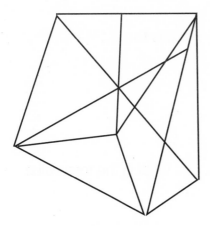

6. Add one letter to complete one word and start the other:

    DAN (...) NIT

7. How many more 5s are in the box than 4s?

3	1	2	3	1	2	3	1
2	5	5	4	66	5	3	5
2	5	3	3	77	1	4	2
3	4	1	4	88	5	2	5
1	3	2	2	1	2	4	3

8.   What is the next number? 289, 225, 169, 121, 81, ?

9.   A supermarket gives shoppers a 75p voucher for every £20 spent. If a shopper spends £120, in pounds and pence, what is the value of the voucher?

10.   How many squares can you see?

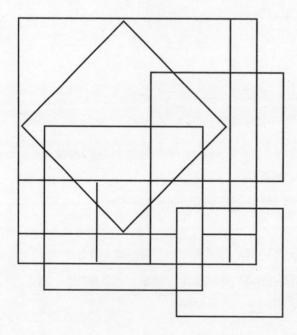

HISTORY

1. Selim the First took control of which empire in 1512?

2. Who was the first woman to take her seat in the British House of Commons?

3. In Greek tragedy, the Furies are known by which Greek name?

4. What was the real name of the children's author Lewis Carroll?

5. What, in millions, was the population of Great Britain in 1901?

6. What name is given to the agreement, regarding the Northern Ireland Peace Process, signed on 10 April 1998?

7. Charlie Chaplin was amongst the founders of which studio in 1919?

8. Who wrote *A Vindication of the Rights of Woman*, which was published in 1792?

9. Which South American country did the Portuguese explorer Pedro Alvares Cabral sight on 22 April 1500?

10. In Athens, free men who were not born in the city were known as what?

GENERAL KNOWLEDGE

1. In a symphony orchestra, what name is given to the key figure who directs musicians using arm gestures?

2. Which Polish-born French chemist was famed for her work on radioactivity and also discovered polonium and radium?

3. In which London church was Queen Victoria's coronation in 1838?

4. Which Olympic sport uses a type of sword, usually a épée, sabre or foil, to hit target areas on their opponent's body?

5. Which animal is sacred to the Hindu religion and is banned from being killed in India?

6.   What is the scientific study of the origin, history, structure and composition of the Earth called?

7.   Francis Crick and James Watson unravelled the structure of which genetic code inside living things?

8.   In which Spanish city would you find Gaudi's famous work the Sagrada Familia?

9.   What is the study of plants, including their classification, structure, physiology, ecology and economic importance called?

10. In physics what is it called when light crosses the boundary between two media with different densities such as air and water?

11. John Alcock and Arthur Whitten Brown were the first to fly an aircraft non-stop across the Atlantic Ocean in 1919, but which aircraft did they use?

12. What is the name of Malyasia's capital city?

13. What is the name of the four operas by Richard Wagner that take approximately 18 hours to perform?

14. Which artist painted *Three Musicians*, in the style of art known as Cubism?

15. What is the name of the first animated cartoon starring Mickey Mouse in 1928?

SCIENCE

1. Which metal has the chemical symbol Pb?

2. What common alloy is made from copper and zinc?

3. Named after the Greek god of fear, which is the larger of Mars's moons?

4. An ohm is the SI unit used to measure what?

5. The volcanically active moon eye-oh orbits which planet?

6. Which class of animals are typically cold blooded, with soft skin, and live in water and on land?

7. What is the name of the liquid fraction of petroleum used in aircraft fuel?

8. The *Beagle 2 Mars* lander that went missing in 2003 was from which country?

9. The iron ore Fe_2O_3, or Iron (III) Oxide, is known by what name?

10. A new rocket being built by NASA for use in the 2020s is called SLS, which stands for what?

ADVANCED LANGUAGE

Solve the following five anagrams:

1. **r a n a y c h**

   General lawlessness and disorder.

2. **i o n f e t e t r u c**

   An imitation designed to deceive or defraud.

3. **s o u r g e v l**

   Very severe or painful.

4. **q u i t e t e t e**

   The forms, manners and ceremonies established by
   convention as acceptable or required in social relations,
   in a profession, or in official life.

5. **n i c e r t o e f y n o c**

   Sweets and chocolates.

SUDDEN DEATH

Calculate: 10 x 7 - 29 x 9 ÷ 3 =

ANSWERS

COMPREHENSION

1. c) The Spanish dance performed by the hidalgo drew gasps from the tourists.
    DEF: a gentleman in a Spanish-speaking country. Prior to the 19th century, a hidalgo was exempt from paying taxes.

2. b) Marnie's eclogue about her holiday in the countryside, was by far her best.
    DEF: a short poem, especially a pastoral dialogue.

3. c) The fugacity of the newspaper headline means that by tomorrow it will be old news.
    DEF: fugacity, noun, the quality of being fleeting or evanescent.

4. a) The proofreader thought she might scream if she had to put in another corrigendum in her book.
    DEF: a thing to be corrected.

5. b) The use of a pleonasm in your essay will bring your mark down.
    DEF: the use of more words than are necessary to convey meaning (e.g. see with one's eyes), either as a fault of style or for emphasis.

MENTAL MATHS
Multiplication
1. 1516.5
2. 840.5
3. 6095.6

Addition
1. 288
2. 358
3. 343

Subtraction
1. 805.5
2. 2676
3. 3667

Percentages

1. 105
2. 195
3. 165

Mixed Calculations

1. 231
2. 602
3. 26

MENSA CHALLENGE

1. Time
2. 40 (11 + 9 + 20 = 40)
3. 74
4. £37.50 (0.75 x 50 = 37.50)
5. 21
6. DAN (K) NIT
7. NB: DANG/GNIT; DANS/SNIT. At least one in each pair is found in Oxford Online, but not in the *Oxford English Dictionary*, so would therefore not be allowed.
8. 2 (5 x 7; 4 x 5)

9.   49
10. £4.50 (120 ÷ 20 = 6 x 0.75 = 4.50)
11. 23

HISTORY

1.   Ottoman Empire (ACCEPT: Turkish empire)
2.   Nancy Astor
3.   The Eumenides (ACCEPT: Erinyes)
4.   Charles Lutwidge Dodgson (ACCEPT: Charles Dodgson)
5.   37 million
6.   Good Friday Agreement
7.   United Artists
8.   Mary Wollstonecraft
9.   Brazil
10. Metics

GENERAL KNOWLEDGE

1.   Conductor (ACCEPT: music director)
2.   Marie Curie

3. Westminster Abbey
4. Fencing
5. Cow
6. Geology
7. DNA
8. Barcelona
9. Botany
10. Refraction
11. *Vickers Vimy*
12. Kuala Lumpur
13. The Ring Cycle (ACCEPT: the Ring of the Nibelung)
14. Pablo Picasso (ACCEPT: Picasso)
15. Steamboat Willie

SCIENCE

1. Lead
2. Brass
3. Phobos
4. Electrical resistance
5. Jupiter

6. Amphibians
7. Kerosene
8. UK (ACCEPT: Great Britain/Britain/England)
9. Haematite
10. Space launch system

ADVANCED LANGUAGE

1. anarchy
2. counterfeit
3. grievous
4. etiquette
5. confectionery

SUDDEN DEATH

123

💡 Did You Know? 💡

Improve Your Vocabulary

Words open worlds. An extensive vocabulary is a powerful one, giving us the ability to communicate, understand language, embrace literature and inspire creativity. Yet improving our vocabulary is often ignored in favour of learning other facts and figures. We don't actively focus on studying new words, but they are the very foundation of a successful education and future. However good we think our vocabulary is it will never be complete, and we can strive to learn new words at any age.

The best way to extend your lexicon is to read. Read more. Keep reading. Whenever and wherever you are, you should have a book with you and turn to that in a quiet moment, rather than to your mobile phone. Read everything, factual, historical, fictional, political, any of the subjects you may normally steer clear of to push yourself out of your comfort zone. It is the quickest, most enjoyable way for you to meet new words that you can commit to memory. Checking them in the dictionary as you come across them means you are more likely to remember by learning in context. Alternatively, make a note of them to refer to later, but don't ignore them.

Using **mnemonic** tricks to learn difficult words can be helpful, like breaking a word into syllables, singing it or rhyming it with something else. However, it isn't just about learning the word; you also need to understand the meaning and where you can use it. A great way to do this is to pick a few new words every day. Write them down and stick them in places where you will see them, like the fridge, a mirror and on your mobile phone, and repeat them in daily conversation. Can you use each of the words five times? Practise by writing them into sentences to make sure you know the meaning as well as the word itself.

Choose word-related board games, puzzles and crosswords to play with your friends and family. You could even challenge someone to a game of Scrabble, endeavouring to include several of your newly learnt words to impress your opponent and win the game!

⚲ Did You Know? ⚲

Learning Physics Formulae and Never Forgetting Them

Being presented with a list of formulae to learn is guaranteed to make the heart sink, however good we may be or think we are at physics. Sorry to say, there are no quick and easy methods for memory success with formulae. Unless we are using them continually, then learning formulae by heart is relentless, difficult and does not necessarily work. Instead, let's look at some of the excellent **mnemonic** tricks we have been talking about – like converting formulae into **acronyms**. Take the simple example of speed=distance/time and remember it as $S = D/T$; or turn it into an **acrostic** sentence using the first letter of each word: Stop Driving Tanks. Another classic formula is force = mass/acceleration or $F = MA$, which could be learnt as Furry Mammoth Animal.

Longer formulae work well broken down in this way too, but also lend themselves to being learnt in a **rhyme** format. Another tip is to look for **patterns** in a formula that you can pull out – like consecutive numbers, alphabetical listing or any strong clues that resonate personally.

Linking formulae to concepts is a great technique. Imagine the visual result of the formula and translate the figures and symbols into words that tell a story. This helps when learning physical formulae like movement and force. Or employ the **Method of Loci** (see page 250), where we visualise the formula in a place we know well, turning it into a set of physical objects that will trigger the memory.

It is daunting to look at a complicated formula, so we need to break it down into basic formulae that we are already familiar with. Don't be afraid to go back to basics and build from there. You can only store and then recall something if you genuinely understand it. Continue to test yourself as you work, play formula games and solve problems. It really is true that practice makes perfect.

Notes